WORKING OUT WITH
WEIGHTS

WORKING OUT WITH WEIGHTS

Produced in association with
International Sports and Leisure
Marketing Limited

COLLINS

First published in 1986
by William Collins Sons & Co Ltd,
London · Glasgow · Sydney
Auckland · Johannesburg

©Sackville Design Group Ltd 1986

Designed and produced by Sackville Design Group Ltd
Sackville House 78 Margaret Street, London W1N 7HB

British Library Cataloguing in Publication Data
Working out with weights
1. Weight lifting
1. David Bromfield
796.4'1   GV546.5

ISBN 0-00-412063-9

Printed in Belgium by Proost International Book Production

CONTENTS

CONTRIBUTORS

Dianne Bennett
Dianne has been involved with weight-training all her life. Her parents, Bob and Vina Woolgar, founded one of the first weight-training gyms in the country in 1935. In 1954, Dianne and her husband, Wag Bennett, opened their own gyms in East London: Wag's for men, and Dianne's for women. Both are taking diploma courses from NABBA (National Amateur Bodybuilders' Association) and EFBB (English Federation of Bodybuilders). Dianne also has a bachelor's degree in physiology.

Stuart Biddle
Stuart has a bachelor's degee in education from Loughborough University, and a master's in science from Pennsylvania State University, USA. He is a lecturer in Physical Education at North Staffordshire Polytechnic, and he has written many articles on the psychology of sport. In addition to his academic qualifications, Stuart is secretary of the Sports Psychology section of the British Association of Sports Sciences, a member of the BAWLA (British Amateur Weight-Lifters' Association) coaching committee and a staff coach for BAWLA. Stuart coaches in various international weightlifting competitions.

David Bromfield
David has been coaching men and women in weight-training to varying degrees of proficiency since 1973. He himself began training seriously with weights in 1964 and began competing as an amateur power-lifter in 1973. Since then, he has coached people in various gyms throughout Devon and Kent. His current projects include the coaching of the inmates in a young offenders establishment for the Kent Probation Service, and working towards selection as a judge for the IFBB (International Federation of Bodybuilders).

George Green
George has spent the last decade working in the health and leisure industry. He is an instructor at the Burton Group Health Club, and has written various articles on exercise and fitness.

Bob Hills
Bob holds over twenty major coaching qualifications, and has been involved in the exercise training field and health and leisure industry for over twelve years. He set up the Burton Group Health Club, which runs a computerised assessment system and organises exercise prescriptions for its members, and has consulted and set up clubs for organisations around Britain.

Rose Macdonald
Rose received a bachelor's degree in physical education and psychology from the University of Western Ontario, and is a Member of the Canadian Physiotherapists' Association (MCPA). She trained as a physiotherapist at Guy's Hospital in London, where she obtained her MCSP (Member of the Chartered Society of Physiotherapists). For many years, Rose taught physical and health education, as well as coaching, on a high school level in Canada. Rose is Superintendent Physiotherapist at the Sports Injury clinic at the Crystal Palace National Sports Centre, and currently lectures on the prevention and treatment of sports injuries, and has published several papers on research related to fitness.

Janice Townson
Janice, who co-wrote the chapter 'Women and Weights', also served as one of the models for the exercise photographs. Before joining the Burton Group Health Club two years ago, she trained with Kay Cornelius, teaching at Pineapple and other dance centres. Janice has trained in many areas of exercise (including a course with 'Birth Centre' on pregnancy as related to exercise and nutrition) and is qualified to teach exercise, healthy eating, weight-training and relaxation.

Mike Winch
Mike has a bachelor's degree in physiology and biochemistry, and three years of physiology research to his credit. He is a BAAB (British Amateur Athletics Board) coach, and has coached for the IAAF (International Amateur Athletics Federation). Mike's primary claim to fame, however, is as one of Britain's top shot-putters since 1973 – in fact, he was in the number one position from 1981-84. He won silver medals in the shot put at the Commonwealth Games in both 1974 and 1982. Apart from all this, Mike is secretary of the International Athletic Club, and he runs a gym at Belgrave Hall in Wimbledon where he also coaches a group of internationals.

INTRODUCTION

The idea of using weights to help us achieve fitness and a better shape has been with us for a long time, but it is only recently that men and women have seen weight-training as a fitness activity in its *own* right.

Up until recently, the general public often confused weight-training (using weights as resistance for muscle tone) with weightlifting or body-building (the use of weights for the specific development of power and muscle mass). Many people would look at a dumb-bell or a barbell and equate it with bulging biceps, steering clear of all weights as a result. Perhaps a residue of doubt has been left in people's minds since the days of the 'before and after' photographs of Charles Atlas, when weights were equated with the building up of the body to Heraclean proportions. Apart from that, its appeal was strictly for men with its catchphrase: "I was a seven-stone weakling, and had sand kicked in my face – *until* I started the Charles Atlas course". What were women to make of that?

Weight-training for muscle tone instead of muscle mass is a very different approach – using lighter weights and far fewer repetitions than the programme followed by body-builders. It is not clearly understood that men (and, even more so, women) would have to go out of their way to achieve the 'muscled' look that frightens off so many people.

At least twenty years ago in America, men and women interested in fitness were using free weights to increase the resistance on their body-toning exercises, and getting quicker results. There were few pieces of machinery, and they now look rather primitive when compared to today's streamlined machines. However, one thing was becoming apparent: weights had a definite role to play in strengthening and toning the bodies of ordinary men and women. People were now exercising in a concentrated way, and not having to do endless repetitions to see results.

Weight-training *can* be undertaken to develop

bigger muscle mass (when it becomes body-building) or more power (when it becomes weightlifting); but this book is for the majority of people who just want to use weights to get in shape and tone up muscles. So what exactly can weight-training do for you? Apart from reducing fat and increasing muscle proportion, it can increase strength, endurance, flexibility and co-ordination; decrease stress; create better poise, posture and body lines; provide your joints with more resistance to injury; help you carry out your daily routine more effectively; and improve your overall fitness. With an improved physical condition come mental benefits: weight-training helps the mind develop better control over the body, thus creating a more harmonious relation-ship between the two. As a result, you look better, move better and feel better – which can only enhance your self-image and sense of well-being!

There are other reasons for taking up weight-training. Some people use it to gain more strength and flexibility in their chosen sport (see Chapter 7, *Get Fit for Sport*). Others use it to help them make a faster, safer recovery from a sports injury (see Chapter 8, *Weight-Training to Recover from Injury*). Still others discover that their social life has improved from working-out with other people: the camaraderie of a gym or club can keep your motivation strong and ongoing. Training with men and women who share the same goals as you, and who can offer their own advice and encouragement, can keep you going long after the initial burst of enthu-siasm has died down (see Chapter 4, *The Pyschology of Lifting Weights*).

An extra word here about *safety*: to avoid muscle strain and muscle tears, warm-up properly before a work-out, stick to a sensible, well-thought-out programme and allow yourself time to cool down afterwards. Learn to distinguish between the stiffness that follows the exercising of sluggish muscles and the sharper pain that indicates something is *wrong*. Stiffness and aching muscles may occur *after* a workout and go away in a day or two; injury pain usually develops *during* a work-out and lingers on. If your pain has not receded by the time of your next training session, check with your doctor, who will advise you when it is safe to begin training again. When you *do* start up again after an injury modify your programme (ie, the poundage or the number of repetitions) so that it will not happen again. *Listen to your body*. It will tell you what it can do, and when it is ready for

more. Best of all, get advice from a professional weight-trainer or coach to ensure that your training regime is right for you.

Today's lifestyle does not require much physical activity, which leaves our bodies in danger of physical decline from lack of use. Most of us lead very sedentary lives – in our work and leisure. And without physical efficiency, our mental efficiency suffers. The great advantage of weight-training is that it can be suited to the individual: you start at your *own* level of fitness – not anyone else's – and work up from there. As you improve, your training programme changes to match it. Weight-training is not about extremes: yes, you can, if you want, train for maximum strength, endurance and power simply by adjusting your poundage and the way in which you train (doing *more* repetitions, for example, or performing them faster), but the choice is up to you. The beauty of weight-training is that it is specific to your needs: in other words, you get what you train for. So, as a *last* word, train safely, train wisely, and have fun!

WHY WEIGHT~TRAINING?

The 1980s may be regarded at a future time as the years people seriously thought about getting fit and *staying* that way. Weight-training is an ideal method, because it encompasses both aerobic and anaerobic movements, which are both vital for complete fitness. Weight-training can provide strength, suppleness and stamina, three qualities that allow you to get the most benefit from your body, no matter what your lifestyle. To improve your body shape, it is not just a matter of dieting down to an ideal weight; the correct fat to muscle ratio must be achieved.

The Value of Exercise

Exercise is contemporary work, and could be considered as today's substitute for work. As changes in culture, society and role-playing take place, and automation has largely eliminated regular, manual labour, our traditional ways to 'work-out' have been replaced by structured and specific 'work-outs' in order to maintain the integrity of our bodies.

Our bodies are designed as mobile machines, and demand our care and attention if we are to enjoy the benefits and longevity of a healthier, fuller lifestyle. Working out with weights must be the logical progression to protecting, maintaining and enjoying our physical bodies, whilst enriching our intellectual and spiritual selves – one facet must not thrive at the expense of another. Our goal is total well-being.

Of course you must apply the rules of good nutrition (choose wholefoods, eliminate additives, take in correct proportions of protein to carbohydrate to fats, plus essential vitamins, minerals and trace elements), but this in itself is not enough. Even achieving and maintaining your 'ideal' weight is no guarantee of health, fitness and aesthetics, if that weight is composed of the wrong fat to muscle ratio – the *right* fat to muscle ratio can only be attained by correct eating paired with correct exercise.

The fittest and most attractive body would swiftly deteriorate into a weak, shapeless mass if confined to bedridden immobility, although fed the choicest and also most scientifically-balanced meals. Life is about movement, and move we must if we hope to achieve the criteria of total fitness. The 'Super Three' qualities for fitness are: Strength, Suppleness and Stamina. To achieve them, we must employ both aerobic and anaerobic movements in our work-outs.

Machines play an important part of any weight-training programme. They work on at least four different principles (see Chapter 5): lever (with chains or cables), cam, hydraulic and Schnell. Below: this bench press machine works on the lever principle.

Why Weight-Training?

Aerobics is concerned with cardiovascular exercise, ie. the development of heart and lungs. The kinds of exercise in which this predominates are cycling, dancing and swimming; in other words, activities that increase stamina. **Anaerobics**, on the other hand, deals mainly with the development of muscle and explosive power. Into this category fall weightlifting, athletic field events, and sprinting – in other words, all sports that have a necessity for above-average strength and power.

It is important to incorporate both forms of exercise into an individual training regime for overall fitness. Most sports and exercise programmes do not encompass both. Not so with **weight-training**, an immensely variable and versatile method of bodywork. Applied in different ways it can provide *both* aerobic and anaerobic movements, be competitive or non-competitive, increase or decrease body size and weight, be a primary pastime, a supplementary training programme, a method of aesthetic body-moulding or a therapeutic tool.

To avoid confusion, let us deal with some of the terms that are often misunderstood:

'**Weight-training**' is a means of exercising to improve performance and physique, whether it be for a particular sport or as a general aid to achieving overall fitness.

'**Weightlifting**' is an Olympic sport which is finite, ie, the winner is the person who can lift the heaviest poundage above the head in a form strict enough to satisfy the three judges.

The term most often confused with 'weightlifting' is '**Body-building**'. This is a sport in its own right, which strives to improve the *aesthetic* appearance of the body in terms of muscle mass and symmetry. It is presided over by the IFBB, (International Federation of Body-Builders), as both an amateur and a professional sport.

Preparation and Clothing

Before you even touch a weight or size up a dumb-bell, make sure that you are not labelled the latter! There should be no food in your stomach for at least two hours prior to training – ignore this direction at your peril. The body's blood supply will always give priority to the digestive system, leaving a deficiency for muscle activity and giving you cramp and nausea, as well as great unpopularity with coach and training partners. By all means drink water, as dehydration is no joke, and eat a piece of fruit after an arduous work-out as this will help replenish your energy.

The criteria for training gear is suitability and comfort – beware of the gym or spa where interest in the latest designer leotard or track-suit rates a higher priority than the warm-up, correct exercise performance or concentration. Easy-fitting track bottoms or shorts in cotton or cotton combination are best, as they can withstand frequent laundering. Avoid tight elastic around ankles or waist, which can impair circulation. A cotton/lycra top or comfortable tee-shirt is ideal, with a track-suit jacket worn on top until you are warmed up. It is important that women keep their breasts supported, but they should avoid overly-tight bras and/or tight straps. Always wear cotton socks to absorb sweat, and good trainers to protect your feet from fungi, bruised toes, and machine friction – not to mention careless training partners. Keep the sweat from your eyes with a headband if necessary, and keep long hair safely confined for comfort. Likewise, dispense with all jewellery of the dangly, dangerous sort: a smack in the teeth with an antique sovereign or semi-strangulation with a golden ingot is not an auspicious start to a training session. It has become popular for lady trainers to use lifting gloves (fingerless types in leather, or the heavy-duty gardening variety), but even men should wear training gloves to maintain a steady grip on the bar and to avoid callus formations. If there are shower facilities where you train, pack a large towel into your training kitbag as well: apart from making you feel better, it will get rid of the sweat and grime and help the muscles to relax.

Are You in Shape?

In preparation for your first work-out, it is imperative that your physical abilities, disabilities and limitations (either genetic or accidental) as well as your individual aims and requirements are considered. Any previous health problem should be discussed and, where any doubt is present, a medical opinion should be sought. In any event,

Half-split banana

1 *Lie on your right side, with your head supported on your right hand, left leg stretched to front as in diagram.* 2 *Bend left knee a little.* 3 *Stretch left leg out again and lift, keeping foot flexed; do not lift too high. Return leg to start position. Repeat exercise 8-20 times, before switching legs.*

Variation press-up

1 *Rest your bottom on your heels and stretch your arms in front of you, knees bent.* 2 *Kneel up, with shoulders over your hands.* 3 *Bend your elbows and bring your chin near the floor keeping body straight. Straighten elbows and return to start position; repeat 10-20 times.*

Warm-up Exercises

Body stretch

1 *This exercise should be done with a partner; sit opposite your partner with feet together and your shoulders square to your partner's. (Alternatively, you can do this exercise alone, placing your feet against a wall.) Inhale and stretch your arms upwards.* 2 *Stretch forwards, exhale, and link hands with your partner (or reach for your toes). Hold for 10 counts. Feel the stretch; then return to a straight-back position with arms raised. Repeat 3 times.*

Bounces

1 *Stand upright with feet apart and parallel, arms stretched over your head.* 2 *Bend your knees, and drop upper body down over your legs. Swing your arms back freely, with your head and neck relaxed. Bounce back to the start position. Repeat 10-20 times.*

13

your rest and exercise pulse rates should be closely monitored, especially the differential between the two. The standard Beginner's programme, consisting of ten basic movements with token weight (which covers the whole anatomy from shoulders to calves) may have to be modified for any individual with a medical problem or limitation. Programmes can be modified according to the information provided on an initial questionnaire. The kind of questions asked might be: age and weight, job and lifestyle, history of illness (accidents and operations), hobbies, sports, pastimes, and so on.

Where to Go

The first thing to decide when embarking on a new fitness regime is the basic one: where to go? During the past few years, a whole new subculture has sprung up to cater for our new-found leisure opportunities and our desire for fitness in all its forms. To satisfy this requirement, hundreds of establishments have opened. These range from offshoots of hotels and clubs which have some basic equipment to huge, purpose-built leisure complexes and health farms which cater, usually in exchange for a hefty fee, for every imaginable kind of activity. The final choice of venue is usually limited to geographical position or the wealth of the trainee.

It is possible to train successfully with weights in your own back garden or bedroom, using the very basic basics – a bar, discs, and dumb-bell rods. The disadvantages are: no tuition, no variety, no competitive encouragement, and no safety factor. Likewise, it is agreed that only the most dedicated and isolated are likely to sustain enthusiasm and regularity in the home environment – the first twinge of fatigue or bead of sweat is enough excuse for most of us to 'down tools', because no one is looking and we have not had to pay any 'subs'. So think seriously about joining the professionals in a gym.

You may be lucky enough to have a weight gym

Jogging machines are a useful piece of equipment, especially when the weather is not suitable for running outdoors. They can be used for warming-up and cooling down, and to supplement a weight-training programme with a strong aerobic work-out. They vary in complexity and price, but the basis of all 'joggers' is a belt rotating around two rollers.

at your place of work, or nearby. There, you will most likely find company, supervision (hopefully), equipment and convenience (showers, driers, etc.). Hopefully the price will be within your means. There may be a municipal complex in your area, which is subsidized and well-equipped, perhaps with part-time instructors and training partners available. It may, however, be crowded, with limited and inconvenient training hours. The super-spas will offer the latest miracle machines, tutelage given by trendy youngsters and magnificent recuperative facilities (leather loungers and potted plants included), but only consider one of these if money is no object. If you are very lucky, you may even discover a value-for-money, middle-of-the-road weight-training gym in your area, with a good lay-out, varied and safe

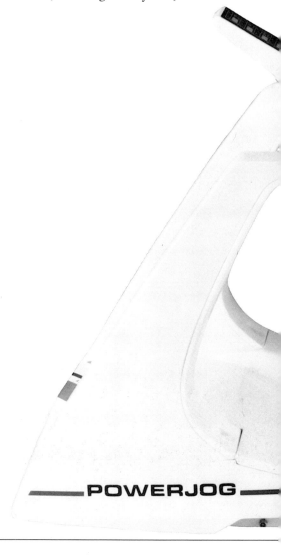

POWERJOG

equipment, plenty of free weights, clean showers and dressing rooms.

However, most people who have trained successfully with weights place 'atmosphere' and good coaching as their two highest priorities. What you should be looking for are enthusiastic, regular training mates and, most important of all, an informed, supportive coach. Do try to ascertain whether or not the person looking after you has a background in the sport and appears both knowledgeable and efficient. Remember that bad habits can creep into your exercise work-outs and severely minimize their effectiveness, and a good coach will prevent this from happening. Do not be blinded by what appear to be tremendous qualifications as there is, as yet, no real governing body that issues qualifications in this sport – so beware, and take notice of the opinions of people who are universally respected in the sport.

Getting Started

We know basically what we want to achieve: a great-looking, good-feeling, active body. Our skeletal structure (bones and joints) is moved by our muscular components (meaty flesh) and held together by our tendons and ligaments. These are maintained in turn by our cardiovascular system (blood = circulation; oxygen/carbon dioxide = respiration). The object of weight-training is to create a healthy cardiovascular system which will enable us to strengthen and tone our muscles as well as reduce our body fat to healthy levels by drawing on stored fat. By using weights we advance from gravity resistance, and maintain 'progressive resistance' which keeps our bodies receptive to improvement and prevents physical stagnation. Let us look at what we mean by 'Progressive Resistance Training' (PRT).

Progressive Resistance Training

Most activities that derive benefit from exercise, such as jogging, cycling and aerobics – provided we do not explore 'quality' aspects of training – may quickly present us with time strictures. When jogging, for instance, an initial two-mile leisurely outing repeated every couple of days, *will* serve to increase our fitness levels. However, if we continue to run at the same pace we will need to run longer distances to achieve the same objectives. This prolonged schedule may well encroach on our non-exercise time – and this is where training with weights (PRT) can come to the rescue.

When we train with calibrated weights (weights ranging from a low to a high poundage), be they on an exercise machine or in the form of dumb-bells and barbells, we work to a set programme of exercise as will be seen later in this book. We first decide which groups of exercises will make up our work-out and we will follow them, using the sets and repetitions principle: each exercise will consist of, say, five sets of ten repetitions. (A 'rep' or repetition is the number of times a movement is performed, and a 'set' contains a fixed number of repetitions. In a set, each repetition is followed by a rest for muscle recuperation.) When a particular muscle-group has got to the stage where it can perform these sets with comfort, rather than having to go back to the quandary facing our jogger with his daily ever-increasing distances, the weight-trainer has only to increase the weight being used to move into a new area of effort.

Thus, simply by increasing the weight and *not* the duration of his work-out, the weight-trainer can continue to develop his potential, by 'progressively' increasing the resistance on the individual muscle groups. Armed with this information, we can now examine the reasoning behind the 'Sets and Repetitions' method.

As muscles develop their potential during the rest following exercise, we need a method of exercising that includes both exercise and rest. Obviously when confronted with the necessity to perform, say, 100 sit-ups, it is unlikely that many people, particularly beginners, would achieve that

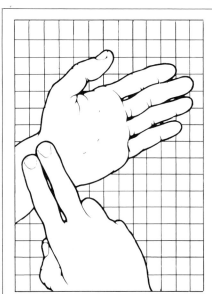

Taking your pulse

At the wrist

Your wrist pulse can be taken by placing the first two fingers just below the base of the thumb inside the wrist, and just above the tendons running up the wrist. Pressing lightly, move the fingers until you feel a steady pulse.

At the neck

To locate the pulse at the side of the neck, place the fingers on either side of your Adam's apple, which is in the groove in front of the muscle which runs vertically down the neck.

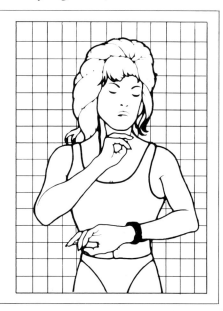

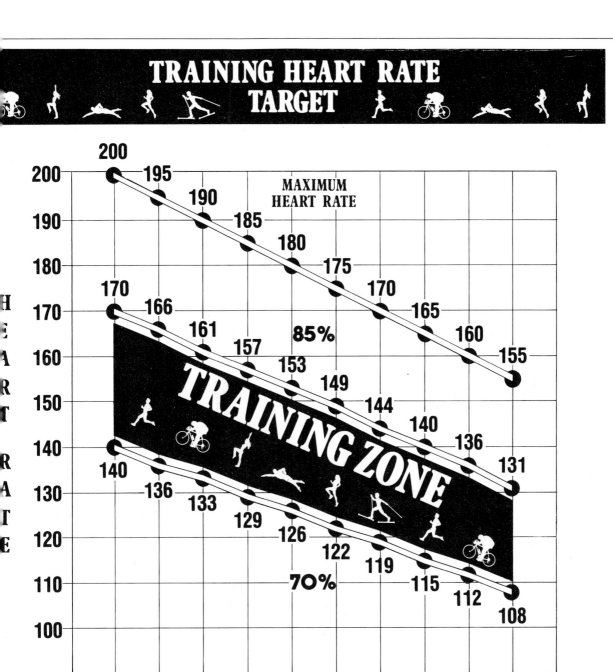

TRAINING HEART RATE TARGET

MAXIMUM HEART RATE

200 195 190 185 180 175 170 165 160 155

85%

170 166 161 157 153 149 144 140 136 131

TRAINING ZONE

140 136 133 129 126 122 119 115 112 108

70%

HEART RATE

AGE
20 25 30 35 40 45 50 55 60 65 70

The material contained in this chart is in accordance with the guidelines set forth by the AMERICAN HEART ASSOCIATION and the PRESIDENTS COUNCIL on PHYSICAL FITNESS and SPORTS

Monitoring your heart rate is the easiest way to determine if you are exercising at an effective and safe level. Each person has a training zone (target heart rate) at which there is enough activity to produce cardiovascular fitness, but not too much to exceed a safe level. The training zone for each individual is between 70 and 85 per cent of maximum heart rate: below 70 per cent, your fitness level will improve little; above 85 per cent, you will get only a little improvement for a great deal of effort and energy.

Maximum heart rate: this is an estimate of the fastest possible rate at which your heart can beat. Reaching your maximum heart rate can be dangerous because you may be working at a harder rate than your heart can handle. **Training zone** (target heart rate): 70 to 85 per cent of your maximum heart rate is the range you should aim for to improve the heart's ability to circulate blood. To find your training zone: beginner (220 – your age x 60%); intermediate (220 – your age x 70%); advanced (220 – your age x 85%).

amount of movement in one go. By splitting the 100 sit-ups into five sets of 20 with a minute's rest in between sets, it not only makes it easier to perform the whole exercise correctly, but it allows the muscles being worked to be re-oxygenated by the flow through them of fresh blood – thus allowing them to benefit from their ability to perform the extra movements. This is made possible by the rest in between. The ideal situation is for the last two or three reps to be fairly difficult to perform, which gives us a gauge by which we can measure our development. When the whole set becomes easy to perform, you simply 'up' the weight.

Starting on the Basic Programme

Presuming then that you now fully understand the principles involved, have no serious medical problems and can set aside a minimum of two sessions a week, we can now go on to discuss how to go about working with weights. There are *two* ways to work out with weights: with machines, or with free weights (dumb-bells and barbells). On the subject of poundage (ie, how much weight to use): if you have a coach, he or she will determine (from your starting strength and degree of fitness) what poundage to begin with; but if you are training on your own, remember to start with the very lightest weight. If that feels ridiculously easy then move up to the next highest poundage: with free weights, this means adding a little more weight to each side of your bar; with a machine, all you need to do is move the pin up one notch (make sure that the pin is pushed all the way in, and that it has not jammed). Remember, too, when lifting machine weights, not to allow the weights to come crashing down on the return-motion – they should touch down gently. You are aiming for a poundage that makes the last few reps difficult but not impossible.

Whichever method you choose, it is *essential* to

start off with a *warm-up*: this allows the muscle groups to become pliant and receptive for the exercise to follow, as well as preventing injury. This can happen when cold, unstretched muscles are pushed through exercises – and the last thing an embryonic weight-trainer needs is a niggling injury in the early days of training which requires him to 'train around' a certain muscle group. You should also follow your exercise programme with a ten-minute *warm-down* period to return your muscles to normal. A little stretching will squeeze the extra blood out of your muscles, and a little cycling will get rid of the lactic acid and improve the circulation. You will feel less stiff, too.

Before we go on to a discussion of what constitutes a warm-up, and the exercise regimes for the beginner, intermediate and advanced weight-trainers (see Chapter 3), let us take a closer look at the main agent being worked upon: the human muscle.

Weight-training taken to the extreme leads to such things as power-lifting, Olympic lifting, and Body-building. **Power-lifting,** *entails training with very heavy weights and competing in contests where the heaviest weight possible is raised above the head;* **Olympic lifting** *involves training with heavy weights but is reputed to have more 'style';* **body-building** *involves lifting weights for maximum muscle mass, to be displayed on an amateur or professional level.*

CHAPTER TWO

THE STRONG BODY

by Mike Winch

The muscles in our bodies are the agents directly affected by the weight-training we do, and to obtain the maximum from our work-outs, it is necessary to understand how muscles are constructed and how they work. With this knowledge, you can also avoid injury, which is the biggest hindrance to successful weight-training. Our physical potential is not often tapped in our daily lives, and physical training can turn the body to a level of performance that will improve all aspects of our lives. With physical fitness comes mental well being.

What are Our Capabilities?

Just how strong is the body? Outwardly, it appears that most people have enough strength in their body to walk around, to stand up and sit down, and to do those things in everyday life that require the minimum of physical effort. But we all have the potential to be super men and women.

This is best exemplified by a true story from America several years ago. A woman was walking along the street with her two children when a traffic accident occurred. A car careered out of control and pinned one of her youngsters to the ground. With no hesitation the hysterical woman lifted the car with one arm and pulled the child free with the other. At eight stones she had lifted over four hundred pounds with one arm, a feat that very few highly-trained male weightlifters could achieve. Needless to say, the aftermath was a severely strained back for this woman – but what a truly superhuman effort!

Knowing this, we must all realize just what physical potential we have in our bodies. How such potential can be tapped is still not fully understood, but it is clear that a combination of mental and physical training can tune the body to an extent far beyond normal capabilities. Such training leads to a far greater harmony within the body and a sense of well-being which must be experienced to be believed.

It is interesting that it was a woman who accomplished this amazing feat of strength, be-cause, generally, our society has assumed that females are the weaker sex. Physiologically, this has some basis in fact since the predominant hormones in women tend to be less anabolic (that is, less chemical builders) and have less of an aggression-promoting effect than do male hormones. In men, these 'masculine' biochemicals are based on testosterone; in the female this is very low in concentration and thus it is far more difficult to utilize protein in both building and strengthening muscle. However, it has become apparent that in recent times women who indulge in hard physical work can slightly alter the body's balance, thus enabling more efficient and rapid progress in muscle development. Concurrent with this hormonal change is a reduction in body fat levels which tend to make the female more slender and muscularly well-defined.

Most sporting coaches know well enough that men have a greater ability to attempt flat-out activities. This again seems to be related to their testosterone levels, and is one of the reasons why it takes a reasonable length of time before sportswomen are able to match their male counterparts in the gym. However, it is becoming clear that the distinctions between men and women which are assumed to have been 'set in stone at birth' are more a matter of social development. In fact, women are now competing with men even in such sports as weightlifting.

This is a great step forward in the social

Muscle guide

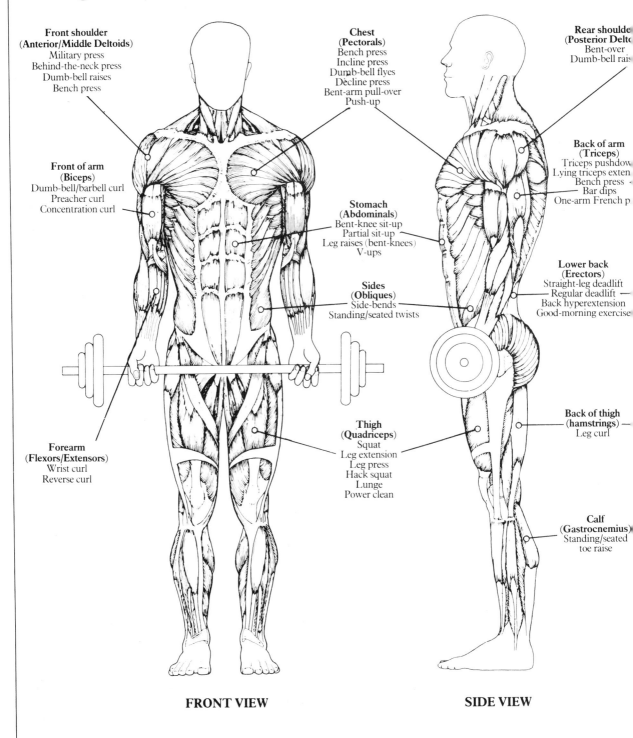

Front shoulder
(Anterior/Middle Deltoids)
Military press
Behind-the-neck press
Dumb-bell raises
Bench press

Chest
(Pectorals)
Bench press
Incline press
Dumb-bell flyes
Decline press
Bent-arm pull-over
Push-up

Rear shoulder
(Posterior Delto
Bent-over
Dumb-bell rais

Front of arm
(Biceps)
Dumb-bell/barbell curl
Preacher curl
Concentration curl

Back of arm
(Triceps)
Triceps pushdow
Lying triceps exten
Bench press
Bar dips
One-arm French p

Stomach
(Abdominals)
Bent-knee sit-up
Partial sit-up
Leg raises (bent-knees)
V-ups

Lower back
(Erectors)
Straight-leg deadlift
Regular deadlift
Back hyperextension
Good-morning exercise

Sides
(Obliques)
Side-bends
Standing/seated twists

Forearm
(Flexors/Extensors)
Wrist curl
Reverse curl

Thigh
(Quadriceps)
Squat
Leg extension
Leg press
Hack squat
Lunge
Power clean

Back of thigh
(hamstrings)
Leg curl

Calf
(Gastrocnemius)
Standing/seated
toe raise

FRONT VIEW

SIDE VIEW

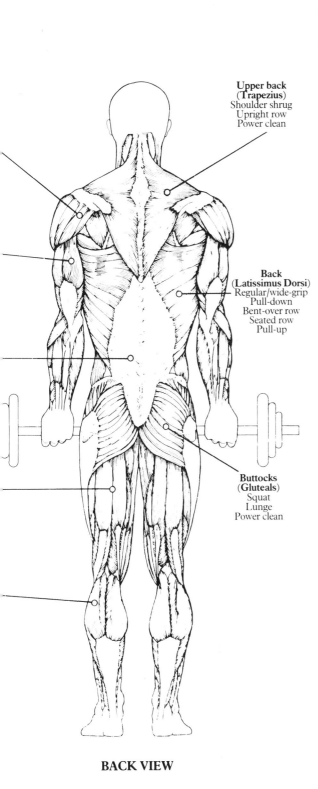

**Upper back
(Trapezius)**
Shoulder shrug
Upright row
Power clean

**Back
(Latissimus Dorsi)**
Regular/wide-grip
Pull-down
Bent-over row
Seated row
Pull-up

**Buttocks
(Gluteals)**
Squat
Lunge
Power clean

BACK VIEW

development of women and there is no longer any reason to assume the physical inferiority of the female sex. This is not to say that there are no structural differences. It is clear that the relatively wider hips of women enable them to become very powerful in the legs, whereas the narrowness in the shoulders tends to lead to comparative weakness in this area. The differences between men and women in these respects are no greater than differences within the individual groups of men or women. There seems to be a continuous spectrum of physical structure and ability.

With the modern trend towards equality of the sexes has come a remarkable increase in the number of women taking part in sport; from mere jogging to the highly competitive strength sports there has been a dramatic change, perhaps motivated by Eastern Europe which has led the way in competitive women's sport. Men are being challenged in all walks of life and their assumed superiority, which has lasted many hundreds of years, is at last being questioned. It is now possible for everyone to train on equal terms. It can only be for the benefit of society if the whole population is involved in the increased consciousness of the value of fitness and health developed through an interest in bodily movement.

The body moves as a result of the action of muscles against the bones, which are the fixed levers of the system. The muscles are held to the bones by tendons, and the bones are held to each other by ligaments. Each part of this system must be kept in tune for the body to work well, and it is through weight and resistance training that this can be accomplished.

What is Muscle?

The muscles of the body make up the basic mechanism by which the functions of the brain are expressed externally. This includes the unconscious actions which maintain the life-support system, such as breathing and the heart's pumping system, as well as the conscious movements resulting from the will to move. These two systems are controlled through separate muscle systems called the *involuntary* (unconscious) and the *voluntary* (conscious) motor systems. The structures of the muscles that make up each system are structurally and functionally different. The involuntary muscles are made up of many single, non-fibrous and separate cells (*figure 1*); whereas the voluntary muscles are made up of long, thin bundles of cells (*fasciculi*), which are groups of cells running parallel to one another in the form of fibre-like structures (*figure 2*).

When the two types of muscle are examined microscopically there are obvious visible differences, apart from their cellular and fibrous natures. The voluntary muscle appears to be *striped* (striated). This can be seen clearly if a tiny

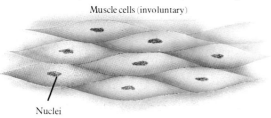

Figure 1 A close-up of cells in an involuntary muscle.

portion of any of the commonly-eaten meats is examined: for example, bacon. These stripes are an important and vital clue to the way in which the muscle works, but it was not until the introduction of the powerful electron microscope that the fine details of structure were elucidated. Up until this time it was not clear exactly *what* the stripes were, or how they formed part of the *contraction* (shortening) process. Detailed visual and chemical analysis of muscle led to the rapid understanding of exactly how the system worked.

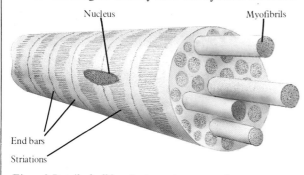

Figure 2 Detail of cell bundles in a voluntary muscle.

If the stripes are examined closely (*figure 3*), it can be seen that they are actually made up of regions of interlinked dense and less dense material. On chemical analysis these prove to be two distinct types of protein called *myosin* (dense) and *actin* (less dense) (*figure 4*). The fibres along which the stripes occur are made up of many cells merged into one (*myofibril*). Bundles of myofibrils form the fasciculi.

The use of proteins to make moving structures

is extensive. This is because by virtue of the infinite number of potential structures that can be formed by proteins, it makes them the ideal material for such a job. There are spherical, ovaloid, straight filament, twisted filament and many other basic forms that proteins can take. Within the muscle fibres the actin takes the form of twisted filaments (rather like wool) and the myosin consists of bundles of straight filaments, giving the latter a microscopically much denser nature. The myosin filaments form chemical links with the surrounding actin fibres. These are made up of golf club-shaped proteins called '*muscle bridges*'. These are really the heart of the muscle's contracting ability.

The bridges shorten or lengthen depending on the state of the muscle. During contraction they shorten, bringing the striations closer together.

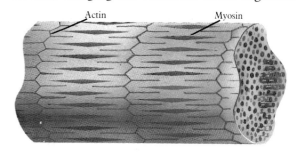

Figure 3 A close-up of the stripes in a voluntary muscle.

This process requires energy which is supplied as a result of the breakdown of energy-rich chemicals within the muscle. These chemicals are broken down as a result of nervous stimulation of the fibrils. The exact nature of this process will be discussed further on.

The Connecting Tissues

For the muscle to work properly, it must be attached to the bones and kept separate from the surrounding tissues. Two distinct types of tissue exist to perform these tasks (*figure 5*).

The *tendons* are the connecting tissues between the muscles and the bones. The bones are rigid and are the levers within the body which enable the force produced by the muscles to be transmitted and translated into bodily movements. A vital task is therefore performed by the tendons in linking the action of the muscles to the rest of the body. Each tendon is made up of strands of a very strong and only slightly elastic

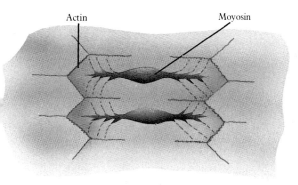

Figure 4 *A close-up of actin and myosin in a voluntay muscle.*

filamentous protein called *collagen*. At the bone end of the connection, the collagen is joined by way of widespread attachments which almost form part of the bone itself. The connection is capable of withstanding some incredible stresses. At the muscle end, the tendon blends into the connecting tissue surrounding the muscle, and therefore has a strong and widespread attachment.

The tissue keeping the muscle separate from its surroundings is called the *epimysium (figure 5).* It is mainly composed of collagen fibres but is slightly more elastic than the tendons so that swelling of the muscle is allowed. It is vital that the muscles are independent of each other and the surrounding tissues, since during complex movement close muscles may need to work independently, and must not interfere with one another. Within the muscle itself, each fasciculum is covered by a sheath of connecting tissue called the *perimysium.* This separates the cell bundles from one another and allows the blood and nerve supplies to have access to the inner parts of the muscle body. Finally, the cells themselves are surrounded by connective tissue called the *endomysium* which keeps each fibre separate and again allows the blood and nerves to reach their final destination.

The connecting tissues therefore have a vital role to play in the mechanical functioning of the muscle, and must not be discarded in any study undertaken. It is often these tissues that cause problems in the trained athlete since they take the stresses of the work more than any other part of the system. This is one of the reasons why warming-up before exercise is important, since it loosens and warms the connecting tissues, making them more pliable and less likely to tear. It is vital for the beginner to appreciate this since injuries can occur by starting resistance work without doing the preliminary loosening and warming.

Energy Systems in Muscular Contraction

Over the years there has been a long and active debate about what exactly *are* the energy sources for muscular contraction. Recently this discussion has been renewed with vigour because it was observed that there seemed to be two distinct types of muscle fibrils within individual muscles. These types are commonly known as *white* and *red* fibres and appear to have very different natures. The red fibres are more heavily invested with blood vessels, and work during slow and extended muscle action. In contrast the white fibres have less blood supply and act during fast muscle action. It has been suggested that the white fibres constitute the 'cold start' mechanism of the muscle. This process seems to be an integral part of all muscular contraction, and it appears that the fast fibres can only work for short periods of time.

The different structure of the two types of fibre seems to indicate that the energy supply in each is different, or, at least, there is a different balance of the several available energy sources. Investigation has shown that the white fibres, since they have little blood supply, must rely primarily on *anaerobic (not* requiring oxygen) energy sources. These include: (a) stored, Adenosine Tri-Phosphate (the high-energy compound, ATP); (b) stored, Creatine Phosphate (the high-energy compound, CP); (c) the combination of two Adenosine Di-Phosphate molecules (ADP) to give one ATP molecule; and (d) freshly made ATP, produced biochemically from the anaerobic

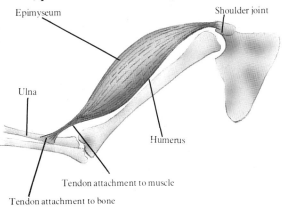

Figure 5 *Details of the tendon and the epimysium.*

breakdown of sugars or fatty acids to form lactic acid. ATP, in all instances, is the direct source of energy and is present in small concentrations within the muscle fibres. It releases its energy by breaking down to form ADP, plus a chemical phosphate group.

The energy thus produced causes the deformation and shortening of the protein which makes up the muscle bridges. This shortening, and thus the overall muscle contraction, can only be sustained as long as this energy is supplied. Once the energy runs out the muscle bridges return to their previous relaxed form and the muscle itself becomes relaxed. Because of the short-acting nature of the white fibres, this does not matter too much. The utilization of the immediately available energy sources described above means that the white fibres can contract quickly, and are thus termed the *fast-twitch fibres*. The red fibres are slow-reacting (*slow-twitch fibres*), but can sustain contraction much longer both continuously and spasmodically. Therefore, although the cause of contraction at muscle bridge level is the same as in the white fibres, the ATP needs to be supplied over a long period of time. The way this is done is through the use of *aerobic* (using oxygen) energy production. Because of this requirement for oxygen the red fibres need the greater blood supply, which is one of their characteristics. The ATP is formed by lengthy biochemical processes called *glycolysis*, the *citric acid cycle* and *oxidative phosphorylation*. These involve the breakdown of sugars and fatty acids to the waste-products carbon dioxide and water. The reactions are far more efficient in producing ATP than are the anaerobic mechanisms, but they are much slower. This fits in with the pattern of slow, long-reacting red fibres.

The ratio of sugars (mainly glucose) and fatty acids (produced from dietary fat, either directly or from stored fatty tissue around the body), depends on the availability of each. Other factors also influence what starting compound is used, such as how long the muscle action has lasted, how much adrenalin is circulating and whether caffeine has been taken close to exercise. Generally speaking, the sugars are more available than the fatty acids because glucose is produced by the simple breakdown of *glycogen*. This is a complex carbohydrate similar to starch, which is made up of glucose molecules joined together. It is actually stored in the muscle and is therefore readily available for the production of glucose and its subsequent use as a muscle energy source. Glycogen is also stored in the liver, but this is used as a general store in case the blood glucose level drops and puts brain function in jeopardy. The presence of stored carbohydrate in the muscle means that until the glycogen is exhausted glucose tends to be the main energy producer. However, both sources of energy are vital for the production of energy in the muscles.

In both red and white fibres there are many microscopic oval particles, the function of which was for a long time unknown. They were called *mitochondria*, and are now known to be the 'power-stations' of the cells. They contain all the necessary chemicals to produce ATP, aerobically, and are probably the most sophisticated chemical energy production systems known. They are thus the centre of activity during aerobic muscle use. During anaerobic activity the energy production takes place in the cell fluid, and thus there is little need for mitochondria in the fast-twitch fibres. However, there are higher concentrations of those chemicals which are needed to produce ATP, in the absence of oxygen.

The Blood and Nerve Supply

The blood supply to the muscles is simple. It consists of a system of blood vessels which resemble a tree, the trunk representing the largest blood vessel and the tiniest twigs representing the smallest. The purpose of the blood supply is to carry *oxygen* and *essential nutrients* to the muscle, and to remove *chemical waste-products* and *carbon dioxide*. The oxygen enters the blood via the lungs (the lungs also remove the carbon dioxide). Similarly, the liver supplies essential nutrients and removes chemical waste-products. The blood is circulating continuously, and therefore the process of supply and removal is going on all the time. The heart is obviously the centre of the circulation, and supplies enough pressure to keep the blood moving throughout the body. During exercise many blood vessels are closed down to allow priority to the muscles. This is the reason why nausea often occurs during strenuous physical exercise – because the blood supply to the digestive system is greatly reduced.

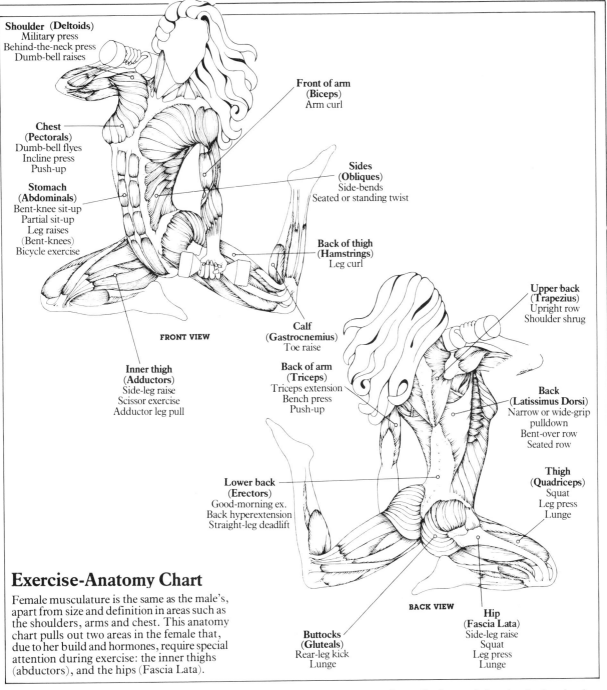

Shoulder (Deltoids)
Military press
Behind-the-neck press
Dumb-bell raises

**Chest
(Pectorals)**
Dumb-bell flyes
Incline press
Push-up

**Stomach
(Abdominals)**
Bent-knee sit-up
Partial sit-up
Leg raises
(Bent-knees)
Bicycle exercise

**Front of arm
(Biceps)**
Arm curl

**Sides
(Obliques)**
Side-bends
Seated or standing twist

**Back of thigh
(Hamstrings)**
Leg curl

FRONT VIEW

**Calf
(Gastrocnemius)**
Toe raise

**Inner thigh
(Adductors)**
Side-leg raise
Scissor exercise
Adductor leg pull

**Back of arm
(Triceps)**
Triceps extension
Bench press
Push-up

**Upper back
(Trapezius)**
Upright row
Shoulder shrug

**Back
(Latissimus Dorsi)**
Narrow or wide-grip
pulldown
Bent-over row
Seated row

**Thigh
(Quadriceps)**
Squat
Leg press
Lunge

**Lower back
(Erectors)**
Good-morning ex.
Back hyperextension
Straight-leg deadlift

BACK VIEW

**Buttocks
(Gluteals)**
Rear-leg kick
Lunge

**Hip
(Fascia Lata)**
Side-leg raise
Squat
Leg press
Lunge

Exercise-Anatomy Chart

Female musculature is the same as the male's,
apart from size and definition in areas such as
the shoulders, arms and chest. This anatomy
chart pulls out two areas in the female that,
due to her build and hormones, require special
attention during exercise: the inner thighs
(abductors), and the hips (Fascia Lata).

The main blood vessels which carry oxygenated blood from the heart are called *arteries*. The biggest is about the size of a small garden hose and has thick muscular walls. They need to be strong to prevent them from swelling significantly under the pressure exerted by the heart's pumping action. From the main arteries there are major branches leading to the important organs of the body as well as the muscles. These branches sub-divide as they reach their destination to form smaller arteries called *arterioles*. At the beginning of each of these is a ring of muscle which is under the control of the unconscious nervous system, which allows the control of blood flow as mentioned above. Within the muscle body the arterioles branch again to form the smallest blood vessels called *capillaries* – these are only just big enough to allow individual blood cells to pass through, and their walls are only one-cell thick. This allows the exchange of gases, water and dissolved biochemicals (sugars, amino acids, fatty acids, minerals, vitamins and hormones mainly), between the blood and the muscle cells.

The capillaries rejoin to form the *venules* (small veins). These in turn join up to form the *veins*, which carry the waste gases and chemicals back to the heart for distribution to the lungs for reoxygenation, and to the liver for detoxification and a new supply of essential nutrients. The whole system is called the *cardiovascular system*.

The efficiency of this system determines to a great extent the aerobic fitness level of the person, and can be dramatically improved by training. Among the effects of training is to increase the size and extent of the blood circulation within the muscle. This results in the trained muscle swelling more than the untrained muscle during exercise. Other effects of training are to improve the efficiency of the lungs in the gas exchanges and to increase the quantity of biochemicals within the muscles which are used in the energy production systems. Often it is found that trained athletes have lower *haemoglobin* (the red substance in blood cells that carries oxygen). This might seem strange, but the blood cells are broken down more rapidly during exercise. The athlete, of course, does not suffer as a result, because the rest of the system is so efficient.

The nerve supply to the muscles (*figure 6*) superficially resembles the blood system by virtue of the fact that large nerves branch and branch again as they near their destination. However, the difference between the nerves and the blood vessels is that the nerves are actually made up of bundles of cells like a telephone wire cable and the blood vessels are single tubes. Each nerve cell has a main body higher up the nervous system and has its own connections to the brain. This actually means that each nerve cell which ends at a muscle cell or group of cells, will behave slightly differently from its neighbours. In terms of maximal nervous stimulation these differences are insignificant, but at lower activity levels very fine control over the extent and duration of stimulation and thus movement can be effected.

The brain's *cerebral cortex* is the starting point for conscious movement. The nerve signals originate here and are passed through the *cerebellum* down the spinal cord and out into the body. The cerebellum is the part of the brain which exerts fine control over the potential movements and is probably the most important part of the brain in relation to the actual control of movement. Parkinson's disease is thought to be associated with biochemical malfunction in the cerebellum. This leads to a lack of control over movement and is exhibited as a constant tremour even when no muscle activity is taking place.

The *spinal cord* is made up of thousands of nerve cell fibres in a bundle. Going down the spinal cord, it can be seen that the cord gets smaller, as each major nerve bundle exits. By the time it reaches the base of the spine there are no nerves left (except those belonging to the cord itself!). Within the spinal cord there are also certain connecting nerves which make up the pathways for *spinal reflexes*. These are reflexes which are produced as a response to stimulation of various *receptors* (nervous receiving points). For example, the patellar tendon has some of these receptors and if they are stimulated by a sharp blow, the message is sent up to the spine where the connections are made to give a response by stimulating the quadricep muscles which straighten the leg. These responses are of significance in sport because many refined movements either need reflex enhancement or elimination. By virtue of the fact that the nervous stimulation starts in the spinal cord and thus has to travel comparatively short distances, reflexes are the quickest movements of the body.

Each nerve running to a muscle tends to be closely associated with the blood vessels in the connecting tissue through which the nerve passes. Each nerve cell ends directly attached to the muscle cells, via a chemical connection called a

Figure 6 The nerve supply to the muscles.

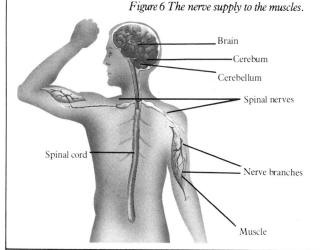

Brain

Cerebum

Cerebellum

Spinal nerves

Spinal cord

Nerve branches

Muscle

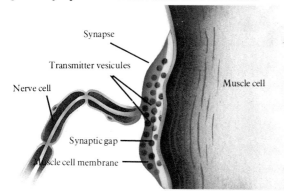

Figure 7 A synapse: a connection between nerve and muscle.

Synapse

Transmitter vesicules

Nerve cell

Muscle cell

Synaptic gap

Muscle cell membrane

synapse. This looks like a flat button on the muscle cell surface (*figure 7*). The gap between the nerve cell and the muscle cell is called the *synaptic gap*. This space is filled with fluid across which the nerve message must be passed. To do this, the nerve cell releases chemicals (*transmitters*) into the gap which have a marked effect on the muscle cell membrane, changing its structure to allow minerals to pass through rapidly. The transmitters are only released as a response to nervous messages coming from the brain or spinal cord.

The way in which this process works is fundamental to the workings of the muscle. The minerals involved are *sodium*, *potassium* and *calcium*. The sodium has a high concentration outside the muscle cell, potassium has a high concentration inside the muscle cell and the calcium sits on the muscle cell membrane, helping to stabilize it. When nervous stimulation occurs, sodium rushes into the muscle cell and potassium moves in the reverse direction. The net result of these exchanges is that the electrical environment within the muscle changes. This in turn stimulates the breakdown of ATP, which in turn releases the energy for contraction. The sodium remains as a stimulus as long as nervous messages are being sent. On cessation of nervous stimulation the minerals are returned to their original concentrations, ATP is no longer broken down and the muscle relaxes. The details of this entire mechanism are not important to understand, but it is vital to appreciate the role of the minerals within the system.

The correct mineral balance in the body as a whole is crucial if efficient muscular activity is required. During prolonged exercise the body loses a lot of moisture and minerals through sweating. At a certain point there are no more reserves to replenish the lost minerals. This is when muscular activity starts being disrupted and symptoms such as a cramp occur. The recent introduction of mineral replacement drinks for sportsmen and women is recognition of the importance of this.

The Skeleton

So far we have discussed the way in which the muscles work, but within the body they would be entirely useless without the presence of the bones. The bones link together to form the basic rigid structure of the body called the *skeleton*. Each person has slightly different bone sizes and lengths which means that only general bio-mechanical principles can be applied to this system. The bones in the limbs are mainly *long bones* such as the *femur, tibia, humerus* and *ulna*. In the places where delicate articulation is needed there are usually a number of small bones such as those in the ankle and wrist. Where protection is needed the bones tend to be flat such as those in the skull and breast bone.

The bone itself is a miracle of biological engineering. The stresses placed upon the bones are huge and yet they are light enough to have the equivalent strength of steel. Where the bones move together at a joint there is a very specialized surface: this is called the *articulating cartilage*. This is a very tough low-friction material which resembles polythene. Like the bone it is a living material, but, unlike the bone, once damaged it does not return to its previous state after repair. This is why it is often less serious to break a bone than to damage cartilage. To keep the joints lubricated they are enclosed in the *synovial capsule* which is filled with *articular fluid*. This fluid also supplies nourishment to the living cells of the cartilage. The thickness of the cartilage seems to be determined in the formative years of childhood, which is why exercise is so important for youngsters. Without it the bones are weak and the cartilage is thin.

The bones themselves are heavily invested with blood vessels and the long bones have central cavities in which blood cells are manufactured. The structure of the bones is under the control of *hormones* which are the body's chemical messengers. The hormones are controlled by the brain: so again there is a direct link between the body's ability to move and the brain. The intricate links that exist to keep the system in equilibrium are called *homeostasis*, a term that encompasses all the balancing mechanisms which are needed to keep the system running smoothly.

THE STRONG BODY

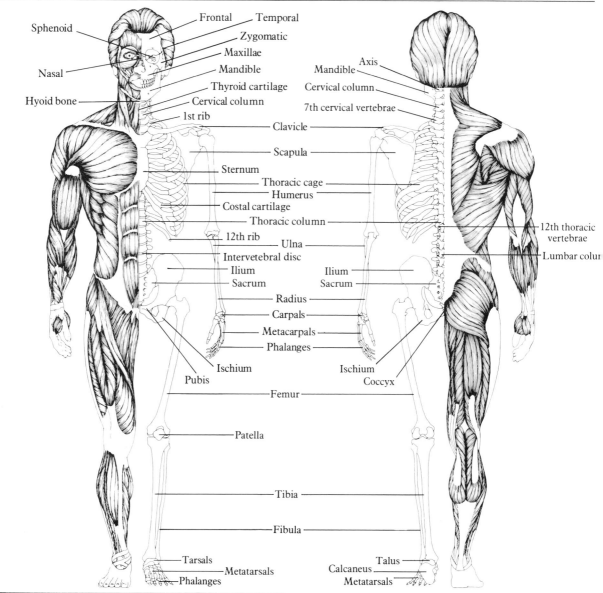

Sphenoid
Frontal — Temporal
Zygomatic
Maxillae
Nasal
Mandible
Hyoid bone
Thyroid cartilage
Cervical column
1st rib
Clavicle
Scapula
Sternum
Thoracic cage
Humerus
Costal cartilage
Thoracic column
12th rib
Ulna
Intervetebral disc
Ilium
Sacrum
Radius
Carpals
Metacarpals
Phalanges
Ischium
Pubis
Femur
Patella
Tibia
Fibula
Tarsals
Metatarsals
Phalanges

Mandible — Axis
Cervical column
7th cervical vertebrae
12th thoracic vertebrae
Lumbar colur
Ilium
Sacrum
Ischium
Coccyx
Talus
Calcaneus
Metatarsals

Summary

It is often considered that the mind and the body are separate. However, it can be seen clearly from our investigations of movement that this is untrue. The intricate links between the brain and the muscles, both directly through the nerves and indirectly through systems such as those involved with homeostasis, clearly show how body and mind work together.

The muscles involved in voluntary movement have the distinct characteristic of being striped. Their cellular structure is a direct result of the way they function in that the stripes are made up of proteins which form the actual contractile material. Microscopic examination gives us further insight into the nature of the muscle in that it has shown us not only the finest details of the contractile mechanism but also the presence of the two distinct muscle fibre types, red and white. The presence of mitochondria in the red fibres gave a clue to the differences in operation between the two types. Further investigation showed that the differences were based on the nature of the energy supply.

The blood supply to the muscles is of vital importance and can be improved with training.

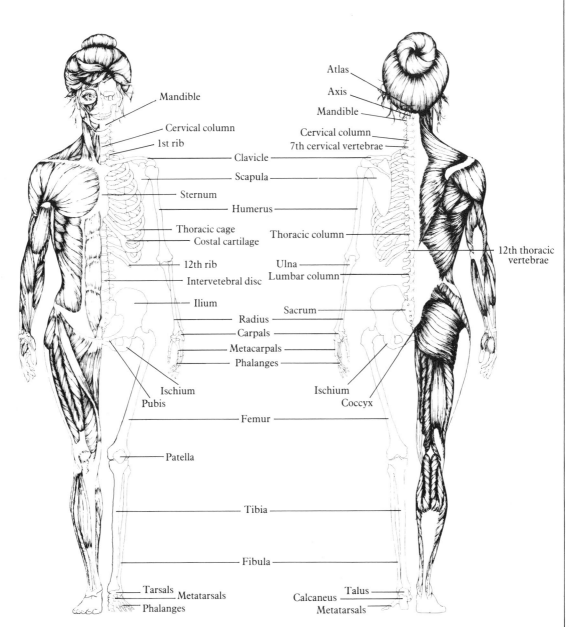

Mandible

Cervical column

1st rib

Clavicle

Scapula

Sternum

Humerus

Thoracic cage

Costal cartilage

12th rib

Intervetebral disc

Ilium

Radius

Carpals

Metacarpals

Phalanges

Ischium

Pubis

Femur

Patella

Tibia

Fibula

Tarsals
Metatarsals
Phalanges

Atlas

Axis

Mandible

Cervical column

7th cervical vertebrae

Thoracic column

12th thoracic vertebrae

Ulna

Lumbar column

Sacrum

Ischium

Coccyx

Talus

Calcaneus

Metatarsals

The capillaries are the points of exchange for nutrients and waste-products between the body and the muscles. The supply of all necessary biochemicals depends on this system being fully operative and working efficiently.

The nervous system provides the conscious link between intention and effect as regards movement. The communication is through chemical messengers. Further connections are made indirectly via the hormone system.

The skeleton forms the solid structure upon which the muscles can act to produce movement. The bones are maintained by hormonal control exerted through the unconsious brain. The joints are a vital part of the whole system, and smooth articulation is made possible by the cartilage.

We can clearly see that bodily movement is the result of complex interactions between all the various operative systems of the body. The seeming simplicity of commanding a limb to move can only be effected if all of those systems work in harmony. The motivation to produce exceptional physical feats can override the normal limits of activity and shows that even untrained and normally weak individuals can do things which they never considered possible.

Shoulder Work-out
Major muscles exercised

SHOULDER
(Deltoids)

Anterior
deltoid
(front)

Medial
deltoid
(middle)

Posterior
deltoid
(rear)

The exercises on these two pages show effective exercises for the shoulder (deltoid) muscles. For general maintenance, perform 2-3 sets of 8-12 reps; for gaining strength and size, perform 4-5 sets of 5-8 reps using heavier weights.

Front dumb-bell raise

1 Hold dumb-bells in front of thighs. 2 Slowly pull one of the weights to the full-flexed shoulder position. The weight should be above your head. Lower weight to starting position, slowly. Now, pull the opposite weight up.

Seated lateral raise

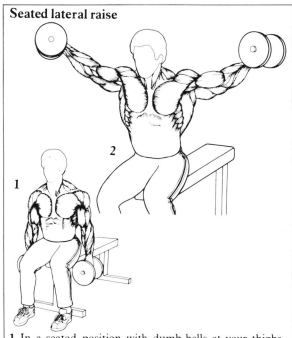

1 In a seated position with dumb-bells at your thighs, strongly contract the front, middle and rear deltoids and pull the weights up directly to the side. 2 Continue to the full-flexed shoulder position, with the weights higher than shoulder level. Slowly lower to start position.

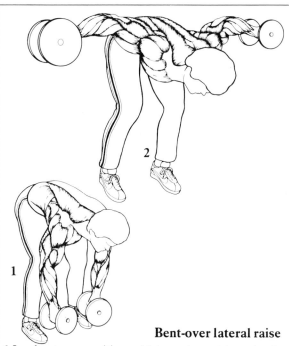

Bent-over lateral raise

1 In a bent-over position, with knees bent pick up dumb-bells. 2 Slowly pull dumb-bells up laterally to a horizontal arm position. Concentrate on using a pulling motion – do not swing the weights. Lower to start position.

Incline raise

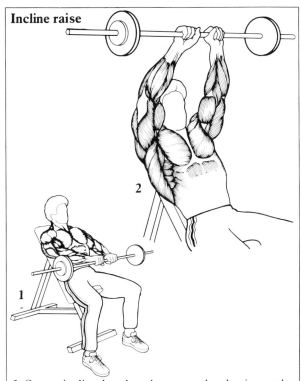

1 On an incline bench, take an overhand grip on the barbell (knuckles up) with the bar just above thighs. **2** Slowly pull the bar up to the full-raise position. Slowly lower to start position.

Lateral cable raise

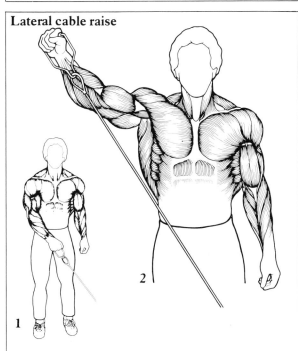

1 Using a one-handled cable, hold handle in front of the thigh. **2** With a powerful, controlled contraction of the shoulder muscles pull the weight up to the side (shoulder height). Complete desired reps. Repeat to the other side.

Alternate dumb-bell raise

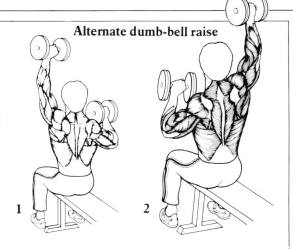

1 Seated, hold dumb-bells as in diagram and slowly press one dumb-bell to an extended arm position. **2** Slowly lower weight to start position. Repeat with opposite weight.

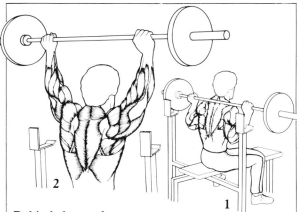

Behind-the-neck press

1 While seated, rest the barbell on your upper back. **2** Slowly press the weight up to a full-arm extended position. Lower the weight back to start position.

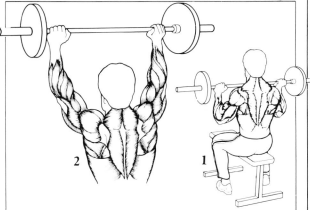

Seated military press

1 Seated, start with bar in front of chin at shoulder height. **2** Drive the weight up to straight-arm position. Slowly lower.

Leg Work-out

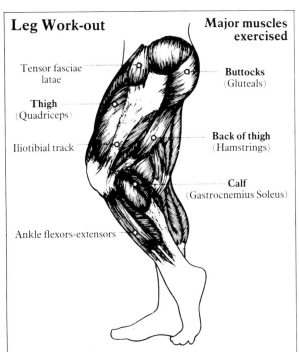

Major muscles exercised

Tensor fasciae latae

Thigh (Quadriceps)

Iliotibial track

Ankle flexors-extensors

Buttocks (Gluteals)

Back of thigh (Hamstrings)

Calf (Gastrocnemius Soleus)

These two pages show some effective leg exercises. For general maintenance, perform 2-3 sets of 8-12 reps; for strength, and size, perform 4-5 sets opf 5-8 reps using heavier weights.

Hack squat

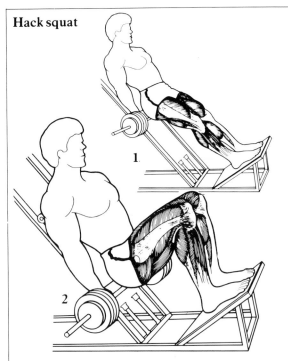

1 Stand on a hack-squat machine with knees slightly flexed. **2** Slowly lower down to a parallel thigh position; then press up to the start position.

Squat

1 With barbell resting on upper back, start with feet pointing out, slightly wider than shoulder-width, and head upright. **2** Slowly lower until thighs are parallel in a squat position. Press back up to start position, but avoid bouncing back up.

Front squat

1 Rest a free-weight barbell on the front of the shoulders. **2** Lower it down until you reach a parallel thigh position. Press back up to the upright position. Repeat. Remember to keep the upper torso, head and spine, upright.

Lunge

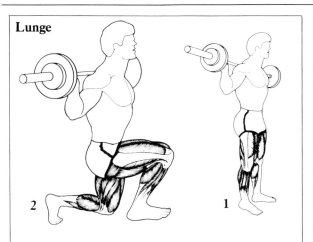

1 With feet apart, rest a barbell on the trapezius muscle. 2 Lower into lunge position, then press back up to start position.

Leg curl

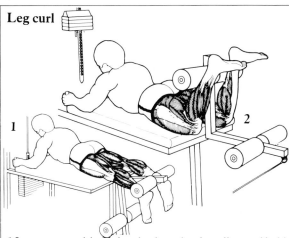

1 In a prone position, place heels under the rollers and hold on to the bench for support. 2 Slowly pull the weight up as close to the buttocks as possible. Return to start.

Leg extension

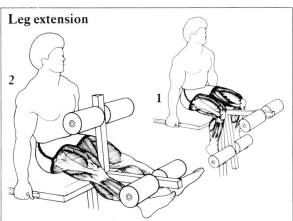

1 In a seated position, slightly lean back with your upper torso and place your hands behind you for support. 2 Pull weight up to a locked-out leg position. Lower weight slowly through a full range of movement.

Leg press

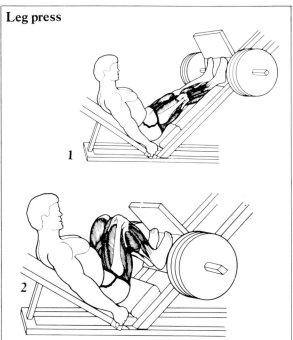

1 In a seated positon, hold on to the hand-grips, and start with legs either extended or bent (depending on the machine you use). 2 Slowly lower the weight to a bent-knee position, then press the weight back to the start position. Repeat. Avoid bouncing, as this may cause injury.

Toe raise

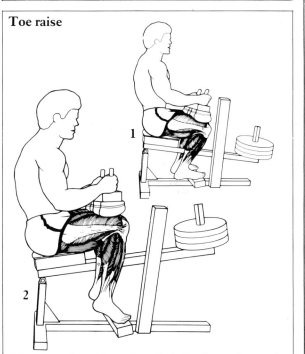

1 In a seated position, place the balls of your feet on the foot supports with knees under the knee pads, and press the weight up to an arched foot position. 2 Slowly lower the weight down until the heels are past the horizontal.

Stomach Work-out

Major muscles exercised

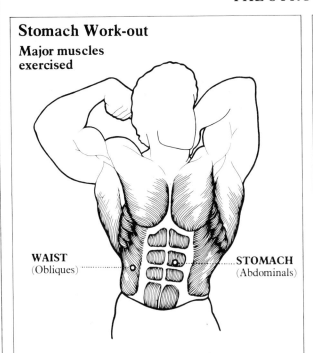

WAIST
(Obliques)

STOMACH
(Abdominals)

The exercises on the following two pages show some of the best ways to shape, strengthen and trim the stomach and waist muscles. Reps and sets will depend on your level of fitness (beginners should start with 2 sets of 8 reps).

Bent-knee sit-up

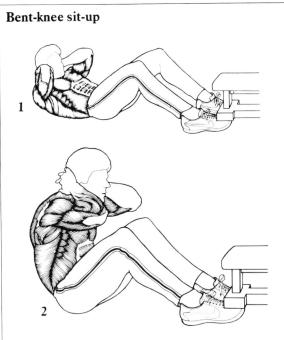

1 Lie on the floor, with knees bent and hands behind your neck, and toes held firm by a low chair/bench. **2** Slowly curl up to your knees: allow the abdominals to contract and do the lifting. Repeat as necessary.

Torso twist

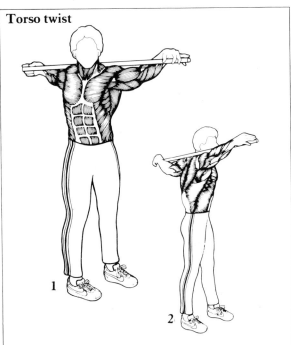

1 Stand with your feet shoulder-width apart, your arms outstretched or with a pole resting on the shoulders. **2** Twist from side to side (feel the oblique muscles stretch), performing an equal number of reps to each side.

Bent-over twist

1 Stand with feet a stride apart, upper body parallel to the floor, arms and knees slightly bent. **2** Pull both arms in a twisting motion to the left; reverse this process to the right. Repeat an equal number of reps each side.

Incline sit-up

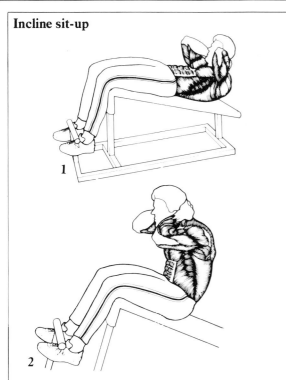

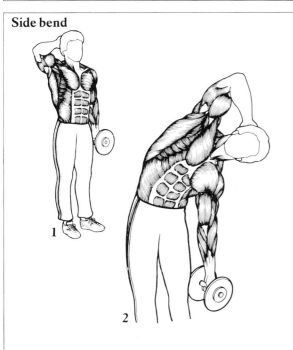

1 Lie on an incline sit-up board with hands behind neck. **2** Slowly curl up to a sitting position, concentrating on pulling with your abdominal muscles. Return to start position. Repeat desired reps.

Side bend

1 Stand with knees flexed, a light dumb-bell in left hand and right hand behind head. **2** Slowly lower to a comfortable side-bend position. Return to start. Repeat all reps to right; change sides.

Knee lift

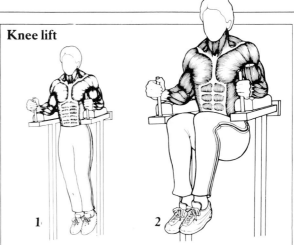

1 Hang from a hip-flexor chair, with your forearms resting on the arm pads. **2** Slowly pull your knees up towards your chest. Return to start.

Partial curl

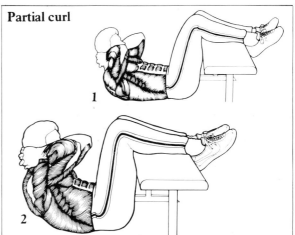

1 Lie on padded surface, with knees bent over a bench, hands behind head. **2** Slowly pull elbows towards knees in a curling motion by contracting your abdominals.

Bicycle

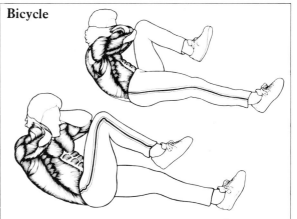

1 Lie on padded surface, hands behind neck and both legs extended. **2** In an alternating cycling sequence, pull one elbow up to your opposite knee. Return to start position and repeat the sequence to the other side. Alternate.

Arm Work-out
Major muscles exercised

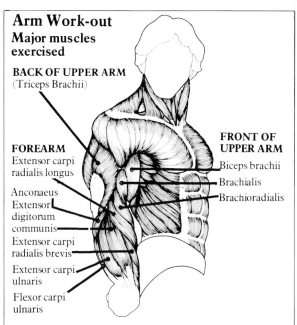

BACK OF UPPER ARM
(Triceps Brachii)

FOREARM
Extensor carpi
radialis longus

Anconaeus
Extensor
digitorum
communis
Extensor carpi
radialis brevis

Extensor carpi
ulnaris

Flexor carpi
ulnaris

FRONT OF UPPER ARM
Biceps brachii
Brachialis
Brachioradialis

These two pages show good exercises for gaining strength, size and shape in the arms. Choose 2 exercises for each arm area. Do 2-3 sets of 8-12 reps for a general work-out; 4-5 sets of 5-8 reps with heavier weights for strength and size.

Triceps extension

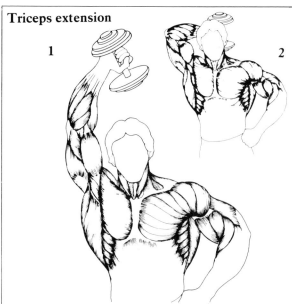

1

2

1 Stand with a comfortable dumb-bell weight held overhead in your extended right arm, left hand on your hip. **2** Slowly lower the weight to a comfortable position behind neck. Then press back up to the start position. After completing your desired reps, repeat to the other side.

Alternate Dumb-bell curl

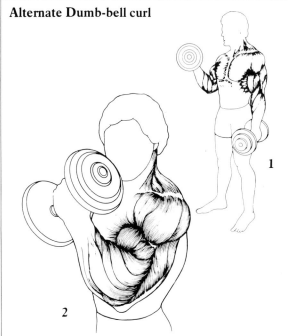

1

2

1 Stand with a light dumb-bell in each hand, palms out, and right arm flexed at elbow. **2** Curl the right dumb-bell slowly up towards your chest, controlling it. Then curl back down to a straight-arm position. Repeat to the left; alternate left and right for the desired number of reps.

Concentration curl

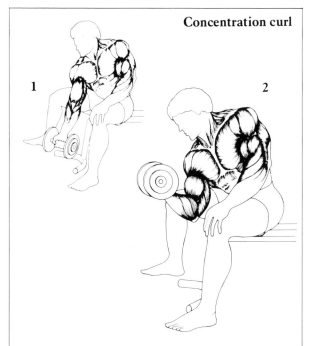

1

2

1 Sit on the end of a bench with a dumb-bell in your right hand and the back of your arm resting on your right thigh. **2** Slowly curl the weight up towards your chest to a full-curl position. Then slowly lower to start position. Perform desired reps before repeating with left arm.

Triceps push-down

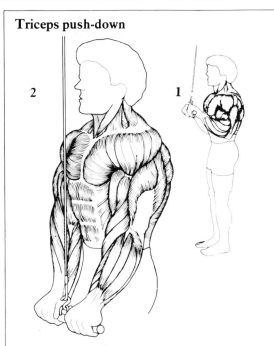

1 Using a machine with an overhead cable/pulley system, stand with arms bent and a palms-down grip on the bar. 2 Using the elbows as a pivot point, press the weight down until the arm is extended. Return to the start; this equals 1 rep.

Lying triceps extension

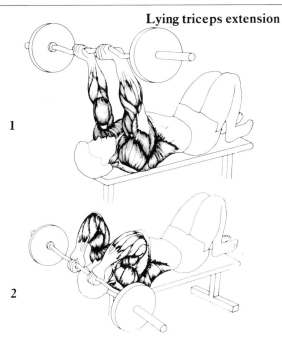

1 Lying on your back with your head and feet on a bench, take a palms-up grip on a barbell (comfortable weight) and extend it straight up with arms locked. 2 Slowly lower the weight behind head towards the floor with arms flexed. Return to start.

'Preacher' incline curl

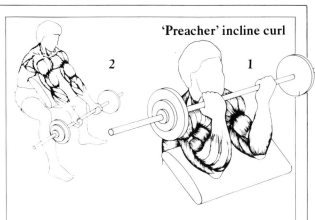

1 Using a light barbell weight, rest the backs of your upper arms on an incline curling bench. 2 Starting from the top, slowly lower the weight to full-arm extension. Pull back up to the start position.

Barbell reverse curl

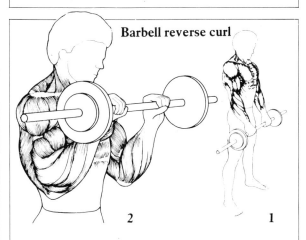

1 Stand with a light barbell at thigh level, with a palms-down grip, arms extended. 2 Slowly curl barbell up to full-flexed position. Avoid swinging the weight up.

Barbell wrist curl

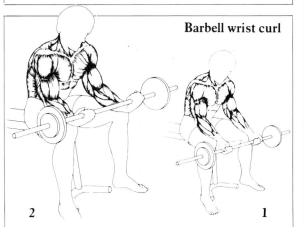

1 Sit on the end of a bench with a palms-up grip on a barbell, backs of forearms resting on your thighs. 2 Slowly pull the weight up to the full-curl position. Avoid swinging the barbell up rapidly. Return to start position.

Back work-out
Major muscles exercised

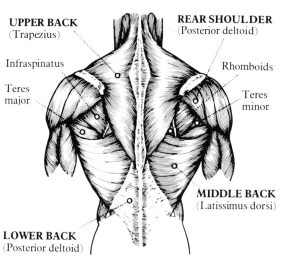

UPPER BACK
(Trapezius)

REAR SHOULDER
(Posterior deltoid)

Infraspinatus

Rhomboids

Teres
major

Teres
minor

MIDDLE BACK
(Latissimus dorsi)

LOWER BACK
(Posterior deltoid)

The following two pages show the most effective exercises for gaining strength, size and shape in the back. For a general maintenance work-out, do 2-3 sets of 8-12 reps; for strength and size, do 4-5 sets of 5-8 reps with heavier weights.

Good-morning exercise

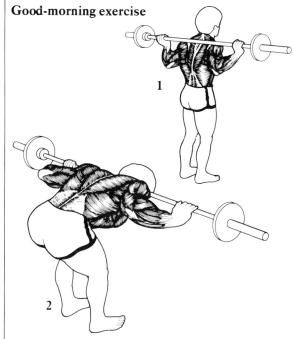

1 Stand with a light barbell resting across upper back (not your neck), with knees slightly bent. 2 Bend your hips and slowly lower your trunk downwards to a parallel position with the floor. Slowly pull back to the start position.

Wide-grip lat pull-downs to the back

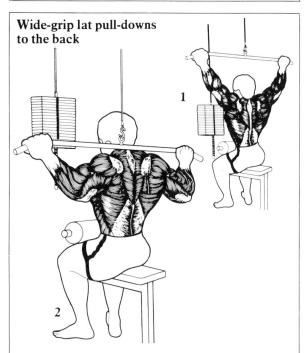

1 Sit on a bench under a wide lat bar with feet placed under the padded rolls, arms extended and hands on the bar in a wide, palms-down grip. 2 Pull the bar down behind your neck (touching the base). Return to the start position.

One-arm dumb-bell row

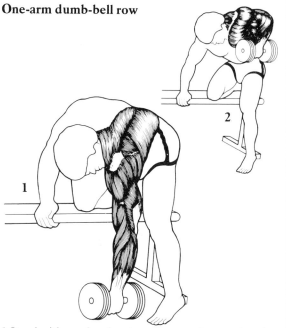

1 Stand with one hand and one knee resting on a bench, a dumb-bell in the opposite hand, arm extended. 2 Slowly pull the dumb-bell up as high to the side as possible. Return to start position; repeat all desired reps before changing sides.

Back hyperextension

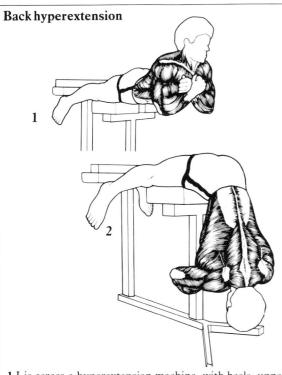

1 Lie across a hyperextension machine, with heels, upper thighs and pelvis supported by the padded rolls, arms folded across chest. 2 Slowly lower your upper torso down as far as possible. Pull up to horizontal position.

Wide-grip chin-up

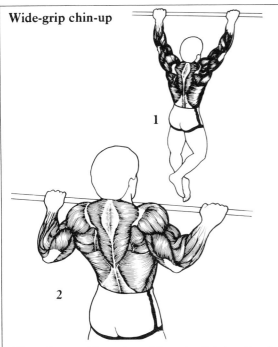

1 Hang from a chin-up bar with a grip slightly wider than shoulder-width, in a relaxed position with feet crossed. 2 With a huge arm and back contraction, pull to the chin-up position. Avoid swinging. Return to start position slowly.

Seated cable row

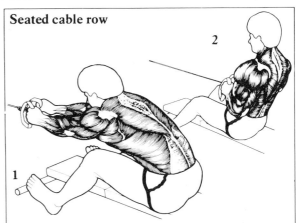

1 Sit on a cable row machine with knees bent, feet supported and arms extended to grip the handles. 2 Pull the handles back into your stomach; avoid leaning back. Return to start.

Bent-over row

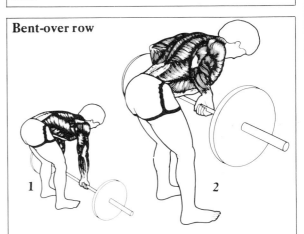

1 Bend over and pick up a weighted barbell with a wider than shoulder-width grip, torso parallel to the floor, knees flexed. 2 Pull weight to chest. Return to start.

Upright row

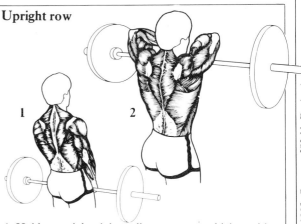

1 Hold a weighted barbell across your thighs, with a palms-down grip, hands together. 2 Pull the bar up to your chin, keeping elbows high and the bar close to your body. Return to start slowly.

Chest work-out

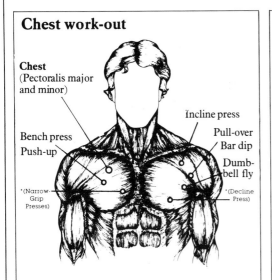

Chest
(Pectoralis major
and minor)

Incline press

Pull-over
Bar dip

Bench press
Push-up

Dumb-
bell fly

*(Narrow-
Grip
Presses)

*(Decline
Press)

Chest Exercise Guide

To develop maximal chest strength and size,
perform each of the following exercises with
the elbows out away from your sides. This
brings the chest muscles into full play. A wide
grip will work the outer chest, a narrow grip
the inner chest.

Bench press

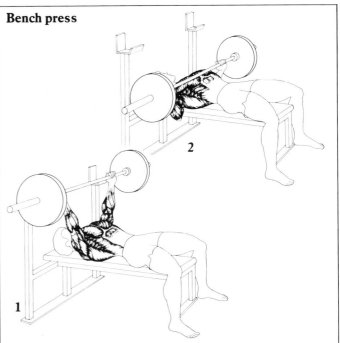

1 Lift the bar off the support racks to the locked-out arm
position; inhale. **2** Slowly lower the bar until it just touches
chest. Press the weight back up to start position without
arching back; exhale.

Incline press

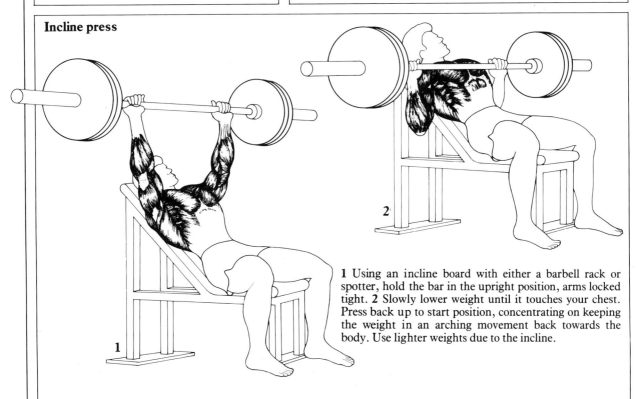

1 Using an incline board with either a barbell rack or
spotter, hold the bar in the upright position, arms locked
tight. **2** Slowly lower weight until it touches your chest.
Press back up to start position, concentrating on keeping
the weight in an arching movement back towards the
body. Use lighter weights due to the incline.

Dumb-bell flyes

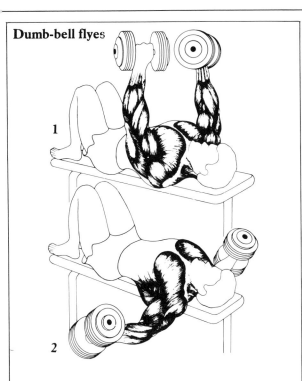

1 Lie on a bench with bent knees, holding two dumb-bells straight above your chest. **2** Bending elbows, slowly lower weights down to sides. Return to start.

Bar dip

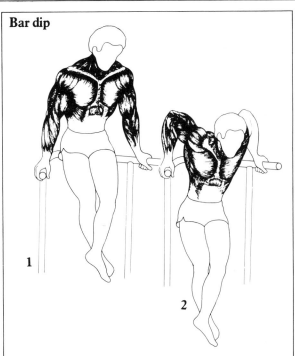

1 Start in an upright position on the bars, with arms locked full out. **2** Lower in a controlled manner, being careful not to bounce at the bottom position. Press back to the start with a chest contraction, elbows out.

Pull-over

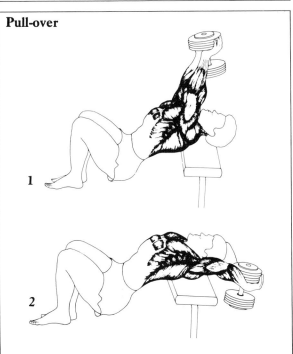

1 Rest your back and head on a bench with one dumb-bell held straight above your chest. **2** Lower the dumb-bell back over the head with a slow, even-paced movement towards the floor. Pull the weight back up with a forceful chest contraction.

Push-up

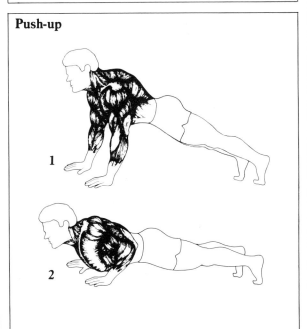

1 Start with hands slightly wider than shoulder-width, arms locked full-out, feet together and head up. **2** Slowly lower your body down until your chest touches the floor. Push your arms up and return to start position, keeping the body rigid (this makes it easier). Repeat as required. (Check with your doctor if in doubt about this exercise.)

THE EXERCISE PROGRAMME

This chapter describes four weight-training programmes in detail: each programme presents its exercises through photographs and clear instructions. Whichever programme you select, be sure to read the safety checklist first ('Points to Remember'), and *always* warm-up before a work-out. If in any doubt about your state of health in regard to weight-training, consult with your doctor first. Weight-training can be fun as well as beneficial, but make sure you understand your own capacity for exercise, and do not overdo it: respect your body and the weights with which you work-out.

The exercise programme is divided into four sections: Beginner's Free Weights, Beginner's Machines, Intermediate Machines and Advanced Machines plus Free Weights. According to your preference or to what is available, choose one of the beginner's programmes before moving on to the next one. If you have had some weight-training experience and feel that you are ready for the intermediate programme, check with your coach first (if you do not have a coach, try any new regime with care, and be ready to backslide to a lighter programme if it is proving too difficult). Whichever programme you choose, make sure that you always warm-up first. This will loosen your muscles and prevent muscle injury. If in any doubt about your state of health, consult your doctor before beginning a weight-training programme. Ideally, you should join a club or a sports centre with a resident qualified coach. Before reading each of the four sections, look at the safety checklist below and follow the guidelines:

Points to remember

Here are some pointers and safety rules to keep in mind when you are working-out. Some apply only to free weights, but most will apply to the other programmes:

1 Perform all movements slowly and smoothly. Be in control of the weight; do *not* let it control you (when using a barbell, for example, do not let it wobble).

2 Start with the recommended number of reps, and work up from there. Your final goal should be three sets of 15 reps.

3 Learn the proper techniques using lighter weights, before you increase the load. You should start off using 7–14kg/15–30lbs. The main rule is that when an exercise becomes easy, you should add more weight.

4 With free weights, make sure that the bars are evenly loaded, that collars are tight and that the weights are secure on the bar. Check that benches are stable. If you are using machines, ensure that the support pin is at the right weight level, and that it is securely in place. When you have finished with a machine, it is courteous to remove the support pin and leave it on top of the weight stack for the next person to use.

5 With free weights, always make sure that your back is flat, whether you are sitting, standing or lying down. Keep your pelvis tilted to avoid a curved spine and lift with your legs to avoid back strain. To keep your back flat on a bench, you may need to place your feet on the edge of the bench, with knees bent.

6 Never train alone with heavy free weights: either use a barbell stand or have someone hand you the weight. In both cases, have someone standing by in the event that you need help – this is especially important with overhead movements and awkward positions (for example, squats with barbell on a block).

7 Work through a complete range of movement.

When using machines, do not let the weight stack come crashing down at the end of each rep; it should touch down smoothly and lightly with the minimum of noise.

8 Work from a position of balance and stability (if working with free weights, the feet should be evenly placed). Concentrate totally on the movement and its correct and steady performance, as well as on the specific muscle group in action.

9 Never hold your breath on an exercise. Exhale during the effort. Follow the appropriate breathing sequence for each exercise if it is given.

10 If adding or removing weights to or from a bar, always do so on the floor.

11 When doing chest exercises, remember that a wide grip will develop the outer portion of the chest, whereas a narrow grip will develop the inner portion of the chest.

12 Work-out only every other day; your muscles will need a day between sessions in which to recuperate. Remember that one session a week will probably not show any results, two sessions a week will show some results, and three sessions a week will show maximum results.

13 Wear trainers to protect your feet (from a dropped weight or from picking up a fungi infection or verrucas), as well as warm clothing to protect the muscles from strain. Dress comfortably so as not to inhibit movement.

14 If you are weight-training to enhance your performance in a particular sport, complete a general body conditioning regime before moving on to the specific exercises.

15 Never train if you feel unwell, have a cold or virus, or immediately after eating a heavy meal. Allow a couple of hours for digestion to start.

16 If you feel any pain, stop immediately, and either lessen the resistance or drop the exercise. Ideally, take advice from your coach.

17 Keep a record of your training programme (exercises, number of sets and reps, and the weight). This will enable you to note improvement, and it will keep motivation strong. Buy a diary now!

18 Always warm-down after a work-out, to get your body back to normal. Some light, rhythmical work allows the muscles to recover more quickly, and it also prevents undue muscle soreness.

19 Be safety-conscious: never fool around with the weights or in the gym. Treat them with respect.

20 Train within your own capabilities: not anyone else's! Learn to listen to your body. You are unique – respect that uniqueness!

Beginner's Free Weights Programme

Assuming that you are warmed-up, a suitable first schedule for a beginner using free weights might run as follows:

1 Standing barbell press (shoulders)
2 Standing lateral dumb-bell raises (shoulders)
3 Bench press with bar (chest)
4 Flat bench flying movement with dumb-bells (chest)
5 Bent-over rowing (back)
6 Biceps curl to shoulders with barbell (arms)
7 Standing side bends (waist)

Tips for bench press exercise

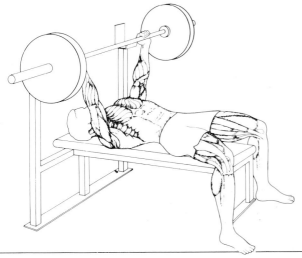

1 Watch out for any unsteadiness of the bar and an uncontrolled return to the breasts or teeth – this is dangerous and uncomfortable.
2 Use a firm, all-fingers-closed grip with dry hands; ideally, use lifting gloves.
3 Concentrate on an even pressing movement; do not allow one stronger arm to give an erratic or imbalanced movement.
4 Take care that the hands are equi-distant from the end of the bar. No lop-sided performance or development, please!
5 Inhale audibly, through the mouth at the start of the movement, and then exhale on the return press.
6 Lock out the elbows, ie, fully-extended arms on each press, but use a slow, controlled movement. No jerking or jarring of the joints.

8 Abdominal raises or sit-ups (abdominals)
9 Squats with bar (upper legs)
10 Alternate dumb-bell calf raises (lower legs)
Note: All exercises consist of three sets of eight reps, but in order to create a more advanced free weights' programme for yourself, the reps should be increased by one per work-out until you reach fifteen. Then you should increase the weight-resistance slightly (ie, the amount of free weights you are using) and start again at eight reps per set.

Strict style is the performance of an exercise exactly by the book and should be used by all beginners.
Cheat style is a variation or loosely applied style which involves other muscle groups and is *not* for the novice.
Cuts is a descriptive term for well-defined muscles, with minimum fat overlay.

Apart from reps and sets, there are a few other terms you need to know about before embarking on your beginner's free weights programme:

A barbell is a length of tempered steel, usually of 1.37m/4ft 6in length (home use) or 1.83m/6ft (gym use), on to the ends of which are added collars (metal locking devices), and required poundage in the form of cast-iron loose weights (discs with a central 2.5cm/1in hole). They range through 1¼ kilos, 2½ kilos, 5 kilos, 7½ kilos, 10 kilos, 12½ kilos, 15 kilos, 17½ kilos, 20 kilos, 22½ kilos and 25 kilos.
A dumb-bell is a 38–45cm/15–18in rod of steel, with attachment as above which enables single-arm movements.
A swingbell is a 38cm/15in rod, with discs centrally positioned to enable a grip at both ends for certain overhead or swinging movements.

A rowing machine – this machine is used primarily to exercise the chest, shoulders and arms, as well as the stomach. It is a machine that can be used at home as well as in the gym.

Left: A Pectoral Deck machine used to exercise the chest muscles, made by Schnell: it is designed, like the Cam and Hydraulic machines, to ensure equal exertion by the muscle through a full range of movement.

Below: This man is exercising on a Module 30 machine made by MultiGym. This company manufactures an extensive range of weight-training equipment.

Beginner's Programme Based on Machines

If you prefer working-out with machines, the following beginner's programme, which includes some bench work, may suit you better than the free weights regime:
1 Bent leg sit-ups (abdominals)
2 In and out (abdominals)
3 Lat pull-downs to the front (back)
4 Standing shoulder press (shoulders)
5 Flat chest press (chest)
6 Waist twists (waist)
7 Biceps curls (arms)
8 Thigh extensions (legs)

Summary
The function of the two beginner's programmes is to gently acclimatize you to working the muscles against resistance. Typically, a period of three to four weeks will be taken up in this way, depending on the frequency of training and your aptitude and fitness levels. At this stage it is vital that the exercises are performed to strict form, as poor technique in the early stages will inevitably mean that the benefits of the exercise are minimized.

During these early stages, a supervisor should be watching closely and adjusting the resistance as any improvements are made. The 'all-body' approach (using all the body's main muscle groups) will form the basis for all further training. This enables you to develop confidence in your body and its potential, and facilitates the transition into the next phase, which is the *Intermediate Programme*.

The Intermediate Programme Based on Machines

The Intermediate Programme is still based on the same principles as detailed earlier, but will also provide you with a wider choice in all training areas. Remember that whatever stage of fitness has been reached, it is still imperative to begin each session with a warm-up. By now, you will have developed a preference for certain warm-up exercises and can adapt them accordingly. A programme for the intermediate weight-trainer might include the following:

1 Roman chair sit-ups (abdominals)
2 Seated chest press (chest)
3 Seated pulley rows (back)
4 Shrugs (shoulders)
5 Triceps push-downs (arms)
6 Leg curls (legs)
7 Calf raises (calves)

When the intermediate level of training is reached, you will have at least two choices of exercise for each muscle-group, and will be familiar with the new disciplines involved. You will also have strong preferences for different exercises. This naturally leads into an area of mixed machine and free-weight use for an individual or *advanced* programme, based upon the criteria of sporting aspirations, personal aims and physical capabilities.

The Advanced Programme Machines and Free Weights Mixed

As basic exercises remain the same throughout your improvement and development, what is now required is a bringing together of the information assimilated so far, and a 'personalization' based upon individual preference.

There are countless variables contained in the broad guidelines so far laid down. For instance, an individual may find that his/her muscles respond better to higher sets and repetitions with only short rests in between, while his/her training partner may discover that lower sets/reps with a longer rest in between suits him/her better. It is a fact that no matter how experienced you may be, you are constantly discovering new factors about yourself and acting upon them. Despite the disciplines required by basic movements there is always room for some flexibility and variation within an individual programme, if for no other reason than to prevent the routines becoming boring or repetitive. Never be afraid to experiment, as the exercises most beneficial to each of us can only be settled upon by trial and error. At this stage then, we are looking for the link whereby your experience can help you choose a regime that fulfils most of your requirements. This is best done in conjunction with your coach, who by now will have probably taken on an almost 'guru-like'

Continued on page 65

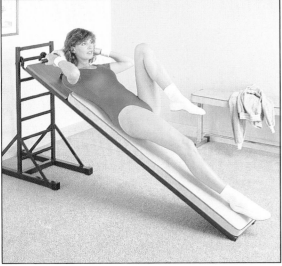

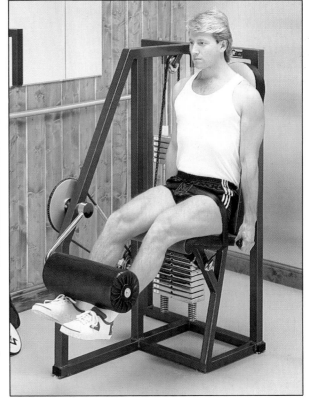

Most weight-training programmes encompass both free weights and machines; it is likely that you will use at least a few machines, unless you are training at home. Benches and boards will almost certainly be used at some point in your programme. Top: this machine is based on the Cam principle used to exercise the backs of the shoulders. Above: a slant board for abdominal exercises with rungs for varying levels of slant/exertion. Right: a leg-extension machine used to exercise the tops of the thighs, again based on the Cam principle.

Warm-up

Here are some typical warm-up movements to stretch and condition the body for exercise. You can warm-up on an exercise bicycle or by using a skipping rope instead – for 5 minutes. Keep the bike on a low setting (eg, between 3 and 4).

Shoulder circles

1 Place your feet a comfortable distance apart, approximately shoulder-width, with the weight evenly balanced. With shoulders pressed down and the back straight, look straight ahead. Keep the arms down at the sides. **2** Then raise the shoulders as far as possible, before rotating them backwards and to the start position. Throughout the exercise, your breathing should be both controlled and comfortable. Three sets of 10 reps.

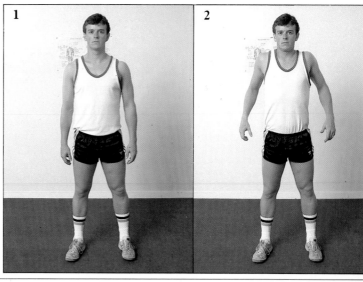

Hip circles

1 Stand straight and erect as in the previous exercise with knees slightly bent. Place both hands on the hips and swing the hips to the side, then forwards. **2** Now around in a circle. Complete the exercise in a smooth fashion, making sure that it does not become jerky. Breathe in a controlled and comfortable way throughout the exercise. Three sets of 10 reps.

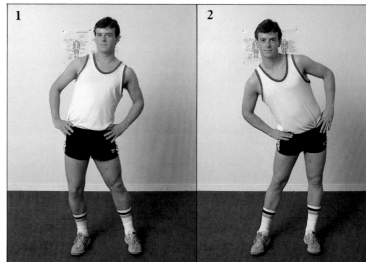

Side bends

1 Stand upright with feet shoulder-width apart and knees slightly bent. Place the hands on the hips as before. Ensuring that only lateral movements take place, bend the upper body to the side. Be careful not to flop to the side but rather lift the body upwards and over to the side. **2** Repeat the exercise bending over to the other side. The breathing sequence should be to exhale as the body moves sideways, and then to inhale as it straightens. Three sets of 10 reps to each side.

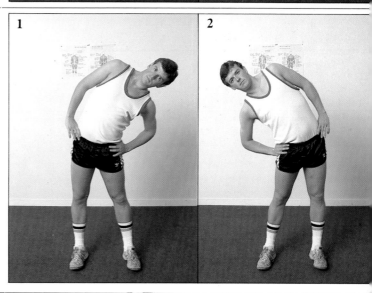

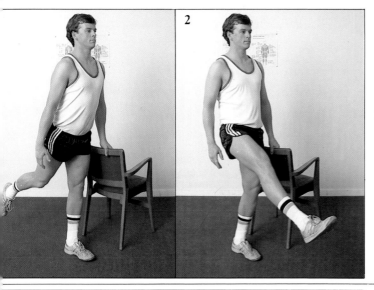

2

Leg swings

1 You need an exercise bar or chair-back. Stand in a straight-backed, upright position with the feet apart. Wiith the bar at your side and the fingers of that hand resting on it for balance (not support), place the other hand on the hip. Move the leg furthest from the bar in a smooth swinging motion, backwards. **2** Now swing it forwards, as far as it will go, keeping a steady rhythm, with the knee slightly bent. Breathing should be controlled and comfortable during the exercise. Three sets of 10 reps with each leg.

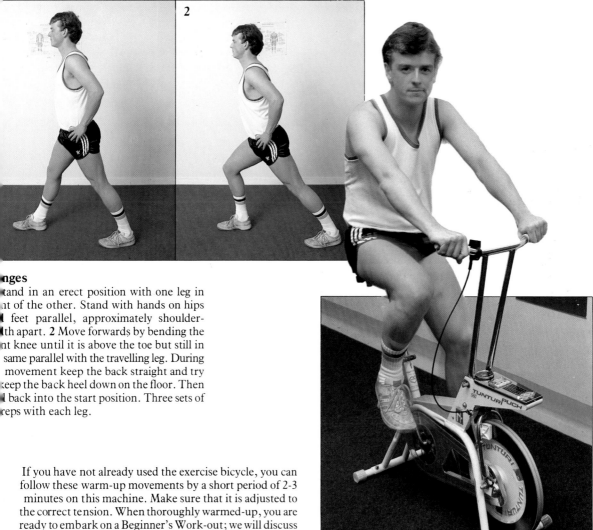

2

nges

...tand in an erect position with one leg in ...nt of the other. Stand with hands on hips ...l feet parallel, approximately shoulder-...th apart. **2** Move forwards by bending the ...nt knee until it is above the toe but still in ...same parallel with the travelling leg. During ...movement keep the back straight and try ...eep the back heel down on the floor. Then ...l back into the start position. Three sets of ...eps with each leg.

If you have not already used the exercise bicycle, you can follow these warm-up movements by a short period of 2-3 minutes on this machine. Make sure that it is adjusted to the correct tension. When thoroughly warmed-up, you are ready to embark on a Beginner's Work-out; we will discuss the programme using free weights *first*...

Beginner's free weights

This programme is based primarily on the use of barbells and dumb-bells. Make sure that you are working with the correct weight, and that it is evenly distributed on both sides of the bar. Check that collars are tight.

Shoulders

Standing barbell press

This exercise works the muscles of the front shoulders, or the Anterior Deltoids. **1** Your feet should be about a pace apart, with knees locked and back straight. Grip the bar evenly across the upper chest a little more than shoulder-width apart. **2** Press the weight upwards and overhead, locking elbows at full stretch and taking care not to lean backwards. Return slowly to the start position. Inhale on the up press, exhale on the return. Three sets of 8 reps each, resting a few minutes between sets.

Standing lateral dumb-bell raises

This exercise works the muscles of the rear shoulders, the Posterior Deltoids. **1** Standing upright with a dumb-bell in each hand, make sure that your feet are 30cm/12in apart. Dumb-bells should be centre front to start. **2** Lift the weights to the sides and just above shoulder-height, keeping the palms facing downwards and elbows slightly bent throughout. Control the return back to the starting position. Inhale on the outward raise, exhale on the downward movement. Three sets of 8 reps.

Chest

Bench press with bar

This exercise works the chest muscles, or Pectorals.
1 Lie on a bench with legs bent, with head and feet supported. Grasp the bar, hands about 60cm/24in apart, with thumbs underneath. **2** Lower the bar from the straight-arm position, touching on the upper chest, then pressing it aloft. Three sets of 8 reps.

Flat bench flying movement (dumb-bells)

This is another exercise for the chest or Pectoral muscles. **1** Lie flat on a bench with a light dumbbell (2-4kg/4-8lb) in each hand, holding them straight up over your chest. **2** Slightly bending the elbows, bring the dumb-bells down until they nearly touch the floor. Then straighten the arms and bring them up again to meet over the chest. Three sets of 8 reps.

Beginner's free weights
continued

Back

Bent-over rowing

This exercise is for the muscles of the upper back, or Trapezius. **1** Bend forwards from the waist with slightly bent knees. Pick up the barbell, then bend forwards from the waist again, letting the arms hang free. **2** Raise the barbell up to the waist, and lower in a rowing motion. Three sets of 8 reps.

Arms

Biceps curl to shoulder (barbell)

This exercise works the front of the arm, or biceps muscle. **1** Stand with feet parallel, approximately 30cm/12in apart for good balance. Bend the knees and pick up the bar with an undergrip, the legs slightly wider than shoulder-width apart. Stand with arms straight, and the bar resting across your thighs to commence. **2** Keep your elbows close to your body while curling the bar upwards and holding it under your chin, before returning to the start position with arms fully straightened. To do this exercise, it is important to resist any swing of the weight or to use the trunk for leverage. Three sets of 8 reps.

Waist

Standing side bends

This exercise is for the 'oblique' muscles at the side of the waist. **1** Stand with your feet apart, with a dumb-bell in one hand and the other hand on your hip. The knees should be bent to protect the back. **2** Smoothly bend to the side, lowering the dumb-bell until a full stretch is obtained. Then return to the perpendicular. Breathe out as you bend to the side and breathe in as you return. In this exercise it is vital that the body does not bend forwards or backwards, but moves precisely to either side. Three sets of 8 reps each side.

Abdominals

Abdominal raises or sit-ups

This exercise works the mid-section, or abdominal muscles. Using the floor initially, or a slightly inclined board, lie flat on your back with knees fully bent and hands clasped behind the head, elbows forward. Attempt to lift your shoulders, chin on your chest, moving towards your knees, which remain bent throughout the movement. Inhale as you sit up, ensuring that the abdomen is contracted as you do so. Exhale on the return controlled movement to the start position. Three sets of 8 reps.

Upper legs

Squats with bar

This exercise works the thigh muscles, or Quadriceps. **1** Hold the bar across your shoulders (but not on the cervical vertebrae), placing your feet parallel, about 30cm/12in apart, with your heels supported on a 5-10cm/2-4in block. **2** Pick a point ahead for concentration, then lower yourself to the floor, keeping your back flat and your head up throughout the movement. Breathe in as you squat, and forcefully and audibly *out* as you push up with the thighs. Avoid bouncing in the squat position, and control the upward push to the return position. Three sets of 8 reps.

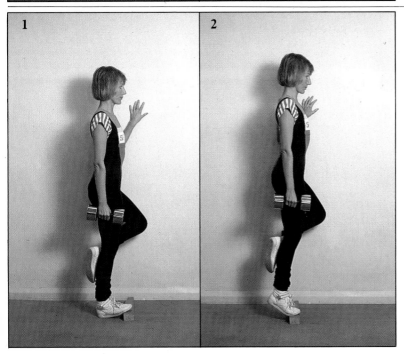

Lower legs

Alternate dumb-bell calf raises

This exercise works the calves, or Gastrocnemius muscles. **1** Stand sideways to a wall with the ball of the outer foot on a block with the heel lowered (the leg nearest the wall is bent and tucked up behind you). Hold the dumb-bell in the hand facing away from the wall. **2** Rise up on the ball of the foot, fully extending the leg. Lower to the start position. Three sets of 8 reps each side.

55

Beginner's machines

This programme will introduce you to the basic machines that you will encounter in a gym or club. Check that the weight is at the right setting before you start.

Abdominals

Bent leg sit-ups

This exercise is performed on a flat abdominal board, and affects the middle and upper sections of the abdominal muscles. **1** Slot the board into the lowest notch, and place the toes of each foot under the rolls at the end. Do not lie flat, as this can cause the spine to 'whip'. Place the fingertips to the temples. **2** Now inhale and curl the head towards the knees. Exhale. Three sets of 10 reps.

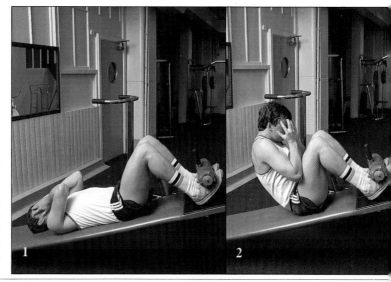

In and out

This exercise is performed on the same abdominal board, but facing in the opposite direction. It affects the *lower* abdomen. **1** With the board on the lowest notch, lie flat on your back with the head towards the captive rolls and the hands gripping the handles above them. Inhale and pull the knees into the chest. **2** Extend the legs until straight, breathing out and pulling the abdominals in, keeping the lower back on the board. Repeat this sequence of bending and stretching for 3 sets of 10 reps, being sure to keep the back flat on the board.

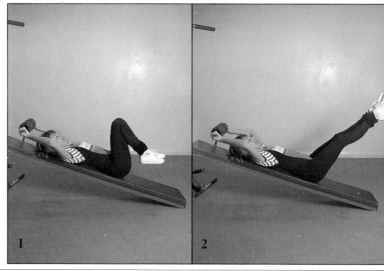

Back

Lat pull-downs to the front

This exercise affects the area in the back known as the 'latissimus dorsi'. These are the two 'wing' muscles extending from under the arms into the upper waist. **1** Using a typical 'lat' pulley machine, hold the wide bar in both hands and pull it down in front of your face. Use an overgrip, sitting on the seat or floor with your feet tucked under you. Allow the spine to stretch fully by reaching up as far as possible with the bar. Breathe in. **2** Slowly pull the bar down level with the chin, keeping the back straight and exhaling during the pull. Breathing in again, allow the weight to return by slowly letting the bar rise back to the start position. Control the bar; do not let the weight do the work. Three sets of 10 reps.

Shoulders
Standing shoulder press
This exercise is for the muscles of the shoulders and upper back. **1** Use a typical 'lever-action' machine with stacked weights, adjusting the upper lever and hand-grips so that they are level with the tops of your shoulders. With legs shoulder-width apart and the body upright, hold the grips with both hands and breathe in. **2** Push the bar up smoothly while breathing out, until your arms are at full stretch. Slowly lower the bar while breathing in, until the start position is reached, but without allowing the weight-stack to rest on the other weights. Three sets of 10 reps.

Chest
Flat chest press
Exercises the chest muscles, backs of the upper arms and front of the shoulders. Use a 'lever-action' machine, with a flat bench at 90° to the weight-stack. **1** With hand-grip levers just above chest, lie flat on bench with head towards the machine. **2** Take the hand-grips and push the bar to arms' length. Return to start position, without weights touching down. Three sets of 10 reps.

Waist
Waist twists
This uses a waist-twister machine: stand on disc with straight arms locked and hands on bar in front. Twist the waist in each direction as far as possible, keeping shoulders parallel to bar. Thirty reps each side.

1

Arms

Biceps curls

This exercise is for the biceps muscle at the front of the arm, and uses a machine with a lower pulley arrangement and a cable attached to a short bar. **1** With feet at a hip-width distance apart, stand straight, and grip the bar in a palms-up position. **2** Keeping your elbows pressed into the body, bend arms at elbow to bring the bar smoothly up to your shoulder. Keeping the muscles under tension, return the bar to the start position. Repeat for 3 sets of 10 reps, breathing in as the bar is raised, and out as it is lowered.

1

Legs

Thigh extensions

This exercise is for the large muscles at the front of the thigh. **1** Using a standard multi-gym leg machine, take up a seated position on the bench with back straight and the backs of your knees right up against the end of the bench. Hook feet under the bottom of the rollers so that the top of the instep is in contact with the bottom of the roll. **2** Slowly, and without jerking, straighten your legs until they are in the fully-extended position; pause, then lower slowly to the start position. Breathe out as your legs are extended, and in as they are lowered. Three sets of 10 reps.

2

Intermediate programme

Once you have mastered one of the two Beginner's programmes, you can move on to a slightly more difficult programme of exercises based on machines.

Abdominals

Roman chair sit-ups

This exercise is for the middle and upper abdominals. **1** This uses a 'Roman chair' machine in a seated position. **2** With hands crossed over your chest, smoothly lean back, taking the strain on your stomach muscles until the body is below parallel. Slowly return to the start position; do not flex the back. Do 3 to 5 sets of 10 reps.

Chest

Seated chest press

This exercises the chest muscles and allows a good range of movement; it uses a Pectoral deck machine. **1** Sit on a stool with the poundage set at a comfortable level. Breathe in and grasp the cushioned arms with hands and forearms. **2** Pull in towards your chest exhaling as you do so. Return to the start position, inhaling. (**Note**: some stools have a bar which will move your arms 15cm/6in forwards so that they are not at 180°.) Do 3 to 5 sets of 10 reps.

Back

Seated pulley rows

This exercises the muscles at the sides of the back, and uses a lower pulley on a 'lat' machine, with a double-handled grip. **1** Sit facing the machine with legs slightly bent and your feet braced on the plates at the base of the machine. Reach forward and grip the double handles. **2** Pull the handles into your stomach using a rowing motion, with back upright. Return the grips to the start position, allowing your torso to move as little as possible. It is important that as the weight is released, the arms should reach out to a full stretch, with shoulders flexing away from the back. Do 3 to 5 sets of 10 reps.

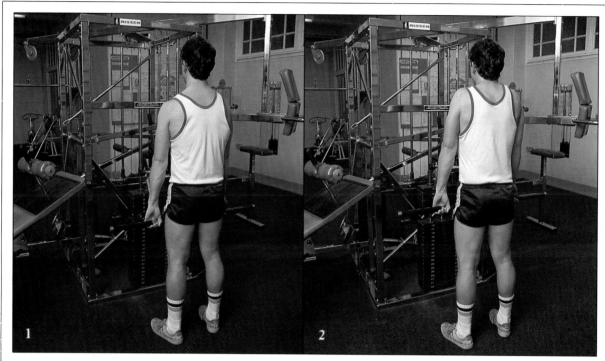

Intermediate programme continued
Triceps push-downs
This exercise isolates the muscles at the back of the upper arm using a fixed pulley machine. **1** Fix a short straight bar to the cable and grip with both hands about shoulder-width apart with palms down. Bring the bar down to the start position with the upper arms vertical, elbows tucked in. **2** Push the bar down until arms are fully extended; return to start position. Do 3 to 5 sets of 10 reps. ▼

Shrugs ▲
This exercises the upper shoulders and upper back muscles. **1** Stand with feet shoulder-width apart; face the machine. Adjust the lever and handles so that the back is slightly bent to grip with both hands. **2** With arms locked and straight, lift up the shoulders to the highest position possible. Rotate them backwards in a full circle. Return to the start position. Do 3 to 5 sets of 10 reps.

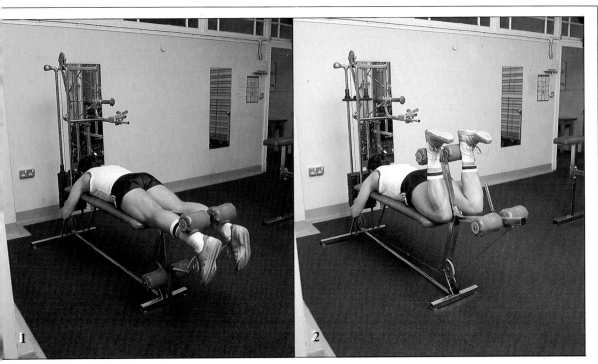

Leg curls ▲
This exercises the muscles at the back of the thigh and is performed on a leg-extension/leg-curl machine. **1** Lie face down on the bench with backs of ankles under the higher padded roll. Grip with both hands under the bench, head on one side so that the spine is as flat as possible. **2** Lift the heels, hold and then slowly lower them until the weight almost touches down. Do 3 to 5 sets of 10 reps.

Calf raises
This exercises the muscle at the back of the calves. **1** Adjust shoulder rolls so that in the start position the weight is lifted just off the stack. With balls of feet on the step, heels as low as possible, place shoulders under padded rolls and hands on grips. **2** Push on balls of the feet so that heels go as high as possible, giving full extension to calf muscles. Then lower to start position. Do 3 to 5 sets of 10 reps.
▼

Advanced programme

You are now ready for the Advanced programme, which is a mixture of machines, benches and free weights. Three sets of 10 reps (15, if very fit) is your aim. Always breathe *out* on the exertion.

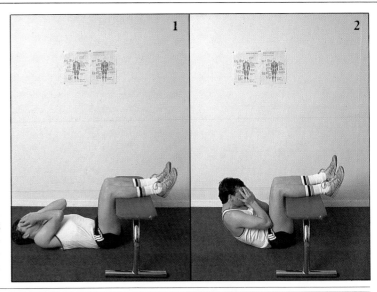

Abdominals

Crunches

This exercises the muscles of the upper abdomen. 1 Lie flat on the floor with the calves supported on a bench. Assume a position where your upper thighs are at 90° to the floor; place fingertips on your temples. 2 Take a deep breath and exhale as you curl your head and upper body towards the bench. Pause; return to the start position. Repeat as required.

Back

Lat pull-downs to the back

This exercises the wide tapering muscles of the back, called the latissimus dorsi ('lats'). 1 Using a 'lat' pulley machine, get a wide grip on the bar and kneel on the floor, allowing your spine to stretch fully with the bar above your head. Inhale. 2 Slowly pull the bar down level with the back of your neck, exhaling. Inhaling again, allow the weight to return by slowly letting the bar rise back to the start position. Control the bar throughout the exercise. Repeat as required.

Shoulders

Upright row

This exercises the upper shoulders and back, and uses a barbell. 1 Take up the start position with your feet shoulder-width apart and your back straight. Hold the barbell in both hands with an overgrip, hands about 10cm/4in apart, and the bar resting against your upper thighs. 2 Keeping the back straight and your head up, slowly lift the bar, allowing the elbows to lead. Keep the bar close to your body. Lift the bar until it is under your chin, with elbows high. Slowly return to the start position. Repeat as required.

Chest

Dumb-bell flyes

This exercise for chest and shoulders, is a modified version of an exercise mentioned earlier (see page 53, 'Flat bench flying movement'). It uses heavier dumb-bells (8kg/18lbs) and a twisting action. **1** Lie flat on a bench with your head supported and the weights held straight above your body, with knuckles facing each other and arms bent. **2** With a flying movement, slowly lower the weights out and down until they are at shoulder level, twisting the dumb-bells half-way through the movement so that your *thumbs* point towards each other. Pause, then return the dumb-bells to the start position, reversing the twisting process as you do so. Repeat as required.

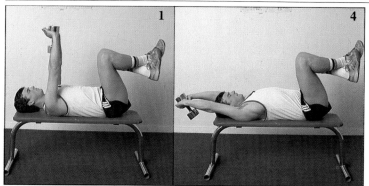

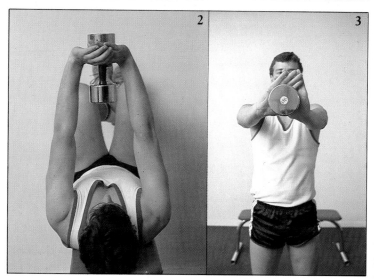

Dumb-bell pull-overs

This exercises the chest and the backs of the upper arms, and uses a heavier dumb-bell (8kg/18lbs) with a special grip. **1** Assume the start position with your upper back lying flat across the bench, using a bent-leg, 'feet-up' position. Grip with both hands on the inside of one end of the dumb-bell, with thumbs either side of the bar and hands interlocked as in pictures **2** and **3**. Hold the weight at arms' length above your chest. **4** Slowly lower the weight down and back until your arms are parallel with the floor. Return to start position. Repeat as required.

Advanced programme continued

Arms

Triceps push-downs (close grip)
This exercises the muscles at the back of the upper arm, and uses the top pulley on a 'lat' machine with a wide bar. **1** Facing the machine with one foot about 30cm/12in in front of the other, grip the bar at chest level with both hands close together and elbows close to the body. **2** Leaning slightly forward with legs braced, extend your hands forward and down, keeping your elbows close to the body throughout the exercise. When your arms are straight down at the front, return the bar slowly to the start position. Repeat as required.

Alternate preacher biceps curls
This exercise for the biceps uses a dumb-bell, and a preacher curl board (or adjustable bench). **1** Sitting down, take the dumb-bell in one hand with your palm facing upwards. Lay the back of your upper arm on the preacher curl board. **2** Keeping the back of your arm on the board, curl the dumb-bell towards you as far as possible; pause, then return the dumb-bell to the start position. The arm should be straightened completely at the end of each movement. Repeat as required.

Legs

Hack squats
This exercises the muscles of the upper thighs, calves, and forearms, using a hack squat machine. **1** With your back pressed flat against the cushion, squat down with a palms-downwards grip on the handles. Your thighs should be parallel to the floor, with feet slightly wider than hip-distance apart and the knees turned out over the feet. **2** Now push up with the thighs, keeping your back flat until you achieve full leg extension. Return to the start position. Repeat as required.

Continued from page 48

importance in terms of advice, support and encouragement.

This chapter is trying to avoid being merely a list of exercises. It is more concerned with laying down basic ground rules and encouraging you to fill in the gaps with the exercises and movements that are most useful to you and which give the best results. Later in this book, individual sports and broad classifications of sports will be discussed. However, at this stage, more advanced exercises are required to lay beside what has gone before – to give a broader choice on which to finalize an individual programme. A programme for the advanced weight-trainer might include:

1 Crunches (abdominals)
2 Lat pull-downs to the back (back)
3 Upright row (shoulders)
4 Dumb-bell flyes (chest)
5 Dumb-bell pull-overs (chest/upper arms)
6 Overhead cable triceps extension (arms)
7 Alternate preacher biceps curls (arms)
8 Hack squats (thighs/calves)

It must be stressed very firmly that the exercises are of vastly greater benefit when completed in strict form. As more experience is gained, you will find the ideal rest periods for yourself. You will instinctively know and feel when the right amount of work is being done.

Conclusion

The four exercise programmes have now been outlined; hopefully they will be a guide to enable the sportsman or woman to select a programme best suited to his or her requirements and aspirations, pointing out the possible pitfalls along the way. They are designed to give a basic grounding in training with weights. There now follows a more detailed look at the exercises in each programme, complete with step-by-step photographs.

Home Gym Equipment

For those interested in setting up a gym at home, or in just owning a few pieces of fitness equipment, the following discussion may prove useful. There is much to choose from on the Home-Gym market, with new products coming out all the time. To avoid confusion and partiality we will discuss *types* of equipment rather than *brand* names. We will start with the smaller items of equipment:

Skipping-rope – you cannot get more basic than this! You can, however, purchase a cheap ordinary cotton rope, or a more expensive leather one which is heavier.

Ankle and wrist weights are weighted bags that strap or buckle to your ankles and wrists and provide extra resistance when doing aerobic exercise. They weigh $\frac{1}{2}$kg–2kg/1–4lbs each, and are made of durable plastic or vinyl. A good set of four is not expensive.

A **Mini-rower** or **'Spring-trim'** consists of two handles with springs attached, at the other end of which are straps to insert your feet. You then row in a backwards movement and (slightly) exercise the stomach muscles.

A **Hip Trimmer** resembles a flying saucer, with straps for your ankles to increase resistance. You stand on it and twist from side to side, working the muscles of the waist and sides of the hips. It is relatively inexpensive.

The **Chest Expander** is based on springs, from three upwards, which you pull in an outward movement to exercise the muscles of the chest. It is a useful piece of equipment and widely available.

A **Power Twister** is a device which is really just a spring with a handle either side: you bend it, and the tension created exercises your arms and shoulders.

A **Chinning bar** is a metal bar that fits across the top of a doorway (self-adjusting), from which you do pull-ups.

Hand-grips are just pieces of sprung metal with handles that fit in the palms of your hands. When you squeeze them, the resistance pushes outwards, exercising your forearms. They are made of metal or high-density foam and are very inexpensive.

The **Bull-Worker** is probably the best-known piece of gym equipment. It is made of metal and based on air-resistance, exercising the upper body. It comes with an indicator scale for measuring performance, and many different exercises can be performed on it. (With the Bull-Worker, you may find that you are paying for the brand name, so shop around – the cheaper ones may be just as good as the more expensive ones.)

Free weights usually come in a set of 50kg/110lbs, with a five-foot barbell and two dumb-bells. The price range varies, but it is worth paying out for a good set.

PROFILE:
VAL AND JOHN FORD
USING WEIGHT~TRAINING TO GET FIT

Val and John Ford are an active, outgoing couple in their mid-thirties, always willing to try new sporting activities. When they moved to Bromley in Kent in 1982, one of their first priorities was to look around for some kind of activity to keep them fit. In their last neighbourhood they had taken part in a keep-fit class and had felt better for it. One day while swimming at Crystal Palace pool in London, they saw a poster advertising the fitness benefits of Masolet Sequence training. Intrigued, they went to see Rose Macdonald, the head physiotherapist at Crystal Palace, who was running the course.

They discovered that the Masolet Programme involved weight-training on five specific pieces of equipment arranged in a circuit. The programme enables you to train and condition the major muscle groups for general fitness, as well as specific muscle groups for particular athletic activities. It had been developed by two Norwegian physiotherapists in the early 1970s, and was originally intended for general physiotherapy work, including rehabilitation for sports-incurred injuries. Rose wanted to see the equipment used to increase the fitness of ordinary men and women, and thus devised a special programme using *circuit training*.

Each of the five machines (leg press, arm press, back extension, arm pull, and abdominal exerciser) would be used for 20 seconds only, with 10 seconds in between to change over to the next machine. Twelve circuits on the five machines, completed in 30 minutes, would constitute a work-out. The aim was to let each muscle group rest as long as possible between periods of exercise in order to build up cardiovascular endurance. It was also convenient for people using the equipment, as no-one could linger on any particular machine, thus creating a smooth flow of people who were each able to work-out equally.

When Val and John expressed their interest in the course, they were asked to fill in a medical questionnaire and to establish their level of fitness with a series of tests: tests for flexibility and strength, as well as for muscular and cardiovascular endurance. (As soon as one's own level of fitness was established, the correct weight level of each machine was worked out accordingly. The system could thus be applied to people of all ages, as a person competes only against himself.) After the testing, Rose showed them how to take their pulse against the clock, and worked out what pulse range they were each aiming for from a table based on their ages and fitness levels. Pulse rates were taken religiously after the last circuit was performed. After demonstrating some good loosening-up exercises and the way in which the five pieces of equipment were to be used, Val and John were ready to go.

Val, in fact, started the Masolet programme first, attending the 12-week course, twice a week. John started up six months later, having kept busy with squash in the meantime. Val remembers that there were six other women in the class, and that Rose was always there to keep a watchful eye on their progress and to offer encouragement. For the first three to four weeks, Val says that she felt 'awful', and needed to lie down at home after each session. Shortly after that, however, she noticed that she felt better in herself, and even John commented that she had 'more bounce'. John was more fit than Val had been when she started the course, but even *he* noticed results in a few weeks when he joined her on the programme: a decrease in weight around the stomach, firmer muscles and a new-found fitness that helped him with his other sports (cricket, squash, tennis and swimming). They were both so pleased with the results that the 12-week course was extended to 18 months! Every six weeks Rose re-tested them for strength and fitness. Val was enjoying the social aspects of the course as well – especially the way in which the cosy, friendly atmosphere created by a small group of people who all had the same goal kept her determined to stick to her own fitness regime. She had tried the weight-training gym at Crystal Palace during this time, and much preferred the circuit training. "Momentum can be lost when you are waiting for a machine to become free", she says, "whereas circuit training allows you to sustain the aerobic element of your work-out with better results."

Val and John stopped training in late 1983, when they were busy setting up their own ski-holiday business together. When the ski season finished in early 1984 they applied for the Masolet course again, only to find that the course was no longer open to the average person: the demand on the equipment by physiotherapy patients had grown too great, and there were no places left. Over the next two years, they both continued with other sports (Val took up ice-skating and squash) and kept up their swimming at Crystal Palace Sports Centre. But something was wrong – they

just did not feel that the level of fitness they had achieved through weight-training had been maintained. Looking back on her year and a half of Masolet training, Val says: "I thought that the exercises were excellent for all-round fitness, and although at first I was using muscles not often used, which made me a little sore, it did not take long to see the difference in my body shape. My energy level improved as well."

In the autumn of 1985, they found a training gym in their area, and started up again. "The atmosphere is not the same as in Rose's class", Val says, "but maybe it will come when we get to know a few people here". In the last months of 1985, they were already feeling the benefits, and ready to cope with another ski season and catering for families on their ski holidays. "When we get back", John says, "we can settle into a more stable training pattern – right now, I am just glad for the stamina benefits it has given us, as we are going to need them!"

Val and John first started weight-training to get fit, but they discovered that it also gave them more energy and stamina for their ski-holiday business.

CHAPTER FOUR

THE PSYCHOLOGY OF LIFTING WEIGHTS

by Stuart Biddle

Weight-trainers often start off in a burst of enthusiasm, only to find that their motivation is flagging after awhile. Often knowing what your goal is, is not enough; you sometimes need more immediate mental stimulation to get yourself to the next work-out, avoiding all the excuses you have lined up for yourself. This chapter will look at the way your mental state can influence the physical performance of your body, the overcoming of mental barriers, 'psyching up' techniques, the psychological aspects of 'looking good', and the various methods you can use to keep motivation strong.

The Body has a Head

It is interesting to note the reactions of people when I mention the activity of lifting weights. If the conversation is about watching the weight-lifters at the Olympics or Commonwealth Games, most people are fascinated by the 'psyching-up' of the competitors at the back of the stage. Remember the back somersault thrown by the Japanese lifter at the Los Angeles Games? A powerlifter from Finland competing at the 1975 World Championships in Birmingham was so 'psyched-up' for his performance that when he came to rub the block of chalk on his hands, he crushed it so hard he created a scene reminiscent of a Christmas card! However, if the conversation with friends turns towards the use of weights for health benefits, then one often hears comments that are psychologically-based, such as "I find that I feel great after a weights work-out … really relaxed" or questions like "I worry about my appearance; can weight-training help?"

These comments show that 'the body has a head'. In other words, many of our thoughts about the lifting of weights, either as a spectator once every four years, or as a regular visitor to the local leisure centre, often involved the *psychology* of the activity and not just the physical factors of how to lift, or what happens to the

muscle as a result of training. Yet despite this, few books give other than a token section to the topic, often covered in a few 'throw-away' lines. So what aspects of psychology might be of use and interest to the user of weights? This chapter will focus on three main areas: the overcoming of mental barriers in lifting heavy weights, including 'psyching-up' techniques; the psychological aspects of 'looking good' through using weights as a means of improving health; and finally looking at the old problem of motivation: how can I stick with a programme of exercises?

Overcoming Mental Barriers

For many years the 'four-minute mile' was an 'impossibility'. Athletes often believed that this barrier was just not humanly possible. Yet within a relatively short space of time after Roger Bannister's historic run in 1954, several runners had achieved 'the impossible'. Today we even have one athlete (New Zealander John Walker) who has run over 100 sub-4-minute miles! The 4-minute mile symbolized the ultimate barrier to be overcome. There is little difference in improving from 4 minutes 1 second to 3 minutes 59 seconds compared with going from 4.03 to 4.01; at least, not in physical terms. However, the psychological transition is a much larger one when a barrier

needs to be removed. The sport of weightlifting has its own barriers; not, of course, as famous as the athletics barriers mentioned above, but the 400lbs snatch and the 500lbs clean and jerk were milestones for lifters in the 1970s. Metrication has changed the barriers now to form an exclusive '200 kilo snatch club' and '400 kilo total club' (lifting 400 kilos in the two Olympic lifts of snatch, and clean and jerk). To date, only one man in the history of the sport has lifted three times his own bodyweight overhead! Imagine it . . . hoisting nearly 400lbs (28.5 stone) overhead and only weighing 9.5 stone!

Beliefs and confidence

Sports enthusiasts have always held the assumption that optimal performance can only be brought about by high levels of confidence and 'believing in yourself'. The 'think positive' slogan is common among coaches. Some situations become so important to the individual that any inhibitions about not being able to handle the task are dismissed, or not even considered. Take the recent case of the Swedish father who returned home from work to find his 18-year-old son trapped beneath his car after carrying out some repairs. The father immediately rushed to the bumper and lifted the front end of the 1700lbs car sufficiently high to allow the son to crawl to safety. The man was not the Swedish powerlifting champion either! In fact, he was recovering from an operation for a slipped disc! The emotion of the situation caused a tremendous physical effort to become a reality. He commented afterwards, "I didn't stop to think", which suggests that he did not have *time* to build up the usual inhibitions and self-doubts we would normally have if faced with the necessity of producing a new best performance as in sport. The Swede clearly displayed 'mind over matter'.

One possible explanation for this may lie in the research on hypnosis. Certain suggestions, both in hypnotic and waking states, can break down the

Opposite: a strong mental attitude is important in power-lifting. Competitors 'psych' themselves up before a lift. Below: enthusiasts believe that 'thinking positive' leads to optimal performance; some situations become so important to an individual that inhibitions are dismissed before they arise.

inhibitions of the body. The central nervous system (CNS) provides a protective mechanism against 'true maximum' performance. Given this gap, therefore, between true maximum and the 'all-out' effort of which we are sometimes capable, a change in expectations or an emergency situation could help reduce this CNS inhibition and thus lead to a superior performance.

The example given above is not, perhaps, that close to many sports events. Certainly in weightlifting a 'blind rage' prior to lifting would result in a poor, if not disastrous, performance. Why? It is well-known in psychology that we need only a medium level of arousal or 'psych-up' to do well in a task. This means that really low levels of arousal, and really high levels also, will not produce the best performance. This is because the ability to concentrate and attend to the task often gets worse when arousal is too high. Of course, this is an over-simplification since some tasks need high arousal (like the lifting of the car), while others need a calm approach (such as the final match-winning pot in snooker). However, the general principle remains true with each task having this 'optimal' level of arousal equating to top performance. This is shown in *figure 1*. As a simplified rule of thumb, activities requiring fine co-ordinated skills need lower arousal levels than those that require gross body movements of limited complexity.

Personal beliefs can also affect your performance. It appears to be more important to consider whether you *think* you can do it. Two sport psychologists from the United States had weight-trainers perform a bench press on a weights machine. Having noted their best performance, they then created (unknown to the subjects, of course) three groups. The first group of trainers was asked to repeat the maximum bench press, but the weight they were told they were lifting was, in reality, slightly less than the subjects believed. The second group was in a similar situation, except that their weight was a little more than they believed. The final group lifted the weight 'blind'; that is to say, they were told nothing about how heavy the weight was. The results showed that subjects who believed their weight to be less than it actually was improved their performance greatly. It appeared, therefore, that the actual weight was less important than

what the subjects *believed* the weight to be. Increased confidence, or a reduction in inhibition, could cause this. Building confidence is not, of course, easy. However, there are several factors that could help:

1 Positive statements: use positive confidence-building statements while lifting weights. We often put ourselves down with negative thoughts. Take a few minutes to practise positive statements (eg. "I've trained hard for this; I'm ready!").

2 Observing others: watching others perform a lifting movement successfully can often give us hints for our own performance.

3 Mental images: practise 'seeing yourself' perform the correct lift (*see* Exercise 1).

4 Let success lead to success: create a successful environment and build up success. Avoid very difficult exercises until you have mastered the easier ones.

Psyching-up strategies

Up until the end of the 1970s, little was known of the content of the mental preparation strategies used by weightlifters and other strength athletes. In 1978, two American researchers from The Pennsylvania State University asked a group of

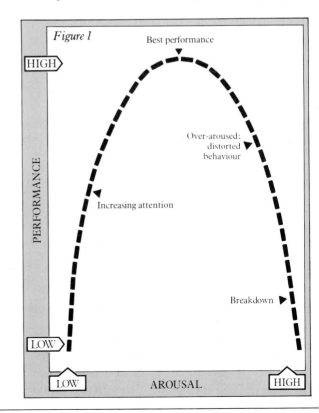

Figure 1

weightlifters to participate in an experiment prior to a competition. They had each lifter squeeze a hand-grip dynamometer (a small instrument used to measure grip strength) and their results were noted. Later they were asked to repeat the activity in one of two conditions. One group was allowed to 'psych-up' before squeezing the dynamometer, while the other group was asked to count backwards in threes from a number given by the experimenter. This was to prevent any 'psych-up' taking place. The results showed quite clearly that the 'psyching-up' was extremely beneficial to performance, while counting backwards produced a slight drop in grip strength. Clearly mental preparation is important to such tasks. But what did the lifters do to psych themselves up? After the experiment, the researchers asked the lifters to describe their personal 'psych-up' strategies. Five main types of 'psych-up' seemed to emerge:

1 Focusing attention: lifters reported trying to 'shut out' any distractions and concentrate on the task in hand;
2 Confidence-building self-talk: here lifters reported talking to themselves in positive ways, such as saying "I can do it; let's go!";
3 Relaxation: some lifters tried to relax, often with results of increased concentration;
4 Mental imagery practice: lifters reported using mental pictures to help 'see' themselves succeed in the task;
5 Arousal: here the lifters said that they tried to 'psych-up' by increasing their arousal and flow of adrenalin through images and self-talk related to 'getting mad' or 'being pumped up'.

Follow-up work by Dr Robert Weinberg and his colleagues from Texas in the 1980s supported these results for another type of strength task. However, when they asked people to 'psych-up' prior to a balance task and a hand-speed task, they found that it made little difference. This suggests that 'psyching-up' is particularly beneficial to strength activities, like lifting weights. This research on 'psyching-up' has shown that the most popular techniques for strength tasks appear to be the attentional focus, arousal, and self-talk strategies. The best performances, however, probably require a combination of many practice sessions with mental imagery, plus a 'psych-up' strategy immediately prior to performance. Exercise 1 will help you develop mental imagery skills (*see* Box 1). It would appear, therefore, that we are

BOX 1

MENTAL PRACTICE OF LIFTING SKILLS

For many years it has been known that just *thinking* about physical movements can help in the learning of the movements themselves, even though no actual physical practice has taken place. Try this exercise and start to develop a better mental picture of lifting skills. More exercises can be found in *Sporting Body, Sporting Mind* (*Cambridge University Press, 1984*).

Stage 1: Relaxation

First of all, find a quiet place and lie down. Try and relax the major muscles of the body by 'letting go'. Concentrate on this feeling of relaxation. After a short while, breathe out slowly and say the word "Relax" after each breath.

Stage 2: Mental imagery

1 'See' yourself at the place where you normally lift weights. Look around and take in the surroundings: people, equipment, colours, etc.
2 'See' yourself perform a simple exercise repeatedly. Note the following guidelines:

★ Perform the movement at normal speed.
★ Use an 'internal' perspective on the image; in other words see yourself lifting the weight as if you are actually lifting (as opposed to seeing on a film).
★ Use as many of your senses as possible; imagine colours, shapes, smells, sounds, etc.
★ Concentrate, as relaxation and imagery are never easy.
★ If the correct image is difficult to keep, do not worry. Just stop the picture and start again. Stay relaxed!

just beginning to understand the psychology of mental 'blocks' or barriers in lifting. Certainly the great lifters of the past have been successful not only in the physical development of their skills, but have also displayed the right mental qualities needed to overcome massively heavy weights. The successful competitor will surely be the one who can effectively combine both physical and psychological strength.

Looking Good, Feeling Good: Health Psychology

In this section, I will consider the psychology of using weights for reasons of health. This is an area of great expansion over recent years with many health clubs and gymnasiums operating throughout the country with both conventional weight-training equipment and modern fixed station apparatus. So why this interest? Probably a major reason is that the media has been constantly reminding us that we live in a 'lazy society'. Health problems associated with lack of physical activity now far out-number infectious diseases. So we find that weak muscles and poor muscle flexibility have led to many back problems; incorrect eating and exercise habits have been associated with heart disease; increased automation has contributed to the need to take exercise as part of our everyday existence, where at one time we got all the exercise we required through our hard physical work.

There is probably more to it than just disease prevention or 'problem solving'. Current trends seem to dictate that a well-developed or shapely physique/figure is desirable, for *both* sexes. Clearly weight-training can contribute to this. People are also discovering that participation in exercise does not have to equate with being excellent at sports. The motto is 'participation not performance', so far more people are getting involved with little embarrassment or feelings of inferiority. This is an important point, since most of our experiences with physical activities at school tend to centre on competitive games, where qualities of skill and high performance are at a premium. Inevitably, many will be left struggling and go away with negative feelings about all forms of physical activity. This is most unfortunate and is a situation that will hopefully change as more individuals participate in personal exercise

programmes and schools initiate the teaching of health-related fitness concepts in physical education lessons.

Feelings about body and self

For many years it has been known that there is a relationship between how we view ourselves and how we view our bodies. Generally speaking, positive feelings about our bodies tend to link with overall positive feelings about our 'self'. Chris Lightbown, writing in *The Sunday Times* magazine in 1981, found that young boy gymnasts clearly demonstrated this link. They all expressed feelings of personal inadequacy (both physical and general) prior to taking up gymnastics training (itself a form of weight-training/physique development). Yet after involving themselves in the sport, and developing physical fitness and competence, they expressed great satisfaction with themselves. For example, one boy, aged 11, said "Now I'm happier and stronger", while another, aged 10, said "... I feel better all the time".

So what is this 'self concept'? It is a difficult term with which to get to grips, but basically it is the way we feel about ourselves and is likely to have been developed throughout life through interacting with other people. It also involves the process of how we *think* other people are seeing us. This process of evaluating ourselves and others goes on all of the time. Indeed, the first time you walk into a gym to lift weights, you are conscious of others 'weighing you up' and assessing who you are. No doubt you do it to others, too! But is there any evidence that all of this relates to lifting weights? The answer, from present research, is clearly 'yes'!

As long ago as fifteen years, a study with a small group of obese teenage males showed that only a three-week physical exercise programme could bring about positive changes in self-attitude, body-attitude, and other physical factors. They also felt that they were closer to their 'ideal self' (ie. what they would like to be) than before the exercise programme. At the same time, a study conducted in West Texas, USA, showed that very fit youngsters were higher in self- and body-concept than a less fit group. Interestingly, they also found that the self-concept of boys was greatly affected by how good they were at sports. This was not so marked with the girls. This suggests that our culture often sees sports participation as more desirable for boys than girls, although happily this seems to be changing. Over 20 years, a study by James Coleman (*The Adolescent Society*), showed that the most highly regarded person in the American school was the top male athlete. A more recent study with college-age women showed that both running and weight-training helped to increase feelings of self-esteem among them.

A series of studies by Dr Larry Tucker, in the USA, gives convincing evidence for the relationship between lifting weights, physique development and associated psychological factors. His initial work in the early 1980s used subjects involved in a weight-training programme twice a week for 16 weeks. Significant gains in many aspects of self-concept were reported by the group when compared with a 'control' group, who did not participate in weight-training. 'Body attitude' scores were also shown to increase. Following up this work, Tucker looked at personality factors as well, and by studying the self and body concepts of some established weight-trainers and non-weight trainers, as well as assessing personality, he found that the stronger individuals were generally more satisfied with their body, more emotionally stable and less anxious, more out-going, sociable and impulsive, and more confident and satisfied with themselves when compared with their weaker counterparts. Whilst I am not suggesting that weight-training is the cure for all evils, it does appear that this form of physical exercise can relate to positive psychological effects.

Relaxation through exercise

It may seem strange to associate exercise, particularly lifting weights, with relaxation, but there is plenty of evidence to suggest that this is the case. As I discuss in the next section of this chapter, we exercise for many reasons, one of which is tension release/relaxation: sometimes called 'catharsis' (a 'cleansing of the emotions'). An obvious case of tension release is to participate in a body-contact sport, like rugby, to release aggression. However, it is not quite as simple as that, as often aggression can lead to further aggression. Also, competitive sports can be quite frustrating, hence create tension rather than *relieve* it! Personal exercise programmes, on the other hand, can have a genuine cathartic effect. This can be for several reasons. First, people develop a sense of competence in themselves, not only physically, but in terms of being able to stick with something worthwhile. Secondly, many people feel physically relaxed after exercise, certainly once they have 'cooled down' and taken a shower or bath. Surprisingly, this feeling can be quite invigorating even when prior to the exercise session you were contemplating skipping the work-out becuase you were too tired! The body seems to over-compensate for the muscular work done in exercising by becoming 'super-relaxed' afterwards. This is shown in *figure 2*.

Exercise can also assist in relaxation as it is a distraction from everyday affairs. Often we get so wrapped up in our work, for example, that a break, created by exercise, can be good for relaxation. This, in itself, is beneficial for health.

American sport psychologist, Dr Dorothy V. Harris, refers to this relaxation/catharsis function of exercise as the 'feel better phenomenon' – something only exercisers can really explain, and something that seems almost incomprehensible to those sedentary individuals who turned off physical activity earlier in their lives. Indeed there is growing evidence for exercisers, particularly runners, to experience quite euphoric states of mind during exercise. This has been linked to the 'positive addiction' concept developed by Dr William Glasser who likened the runner to a meditator in achieving his/her 'daily fix' of exercise. Research at the University of Illinois by Dr Rainer Martens, suggests that experienced runners completing over 40 minutes per run, are more likely to experience these positive effects, and to feel uncomfortable at missing a run. One wonders whether this is also possible in other forms of exercise, such as lifting weights. Whilst it is more likely that continuous activities like running will lead to more 'trance-like' states than intermittent forms of exercise, there is every possibility of similar positive states of mind occurring in the weights room.

Exercise Motivation

Motives for participation

Why do people lift weights? Why do some individuals think weight-trainers are mad to pursue such an activity of their own free will? Such questions concern peoples' *motives* or *motivation to exercise*. Surprisingly, sport psychologists have only a few studies to draw on to answer these questions. Recently, American researchers have been interested in finding out why youngsters participate in, or drop out of, sports programmes. The major reasons for participation appear to be:

1 Achievement of skills.
2 To be with other people.
3 To improve health and fitness.
4 To demonstrate power and independence.
5 To be aggressive.
6 Tension release.
7 To seek excitement and arousal.
8 To compete against others.

No doubt there are many other factors, and some people participate for a combination of these, and other, reasons. Knowing why you want to lift weights will help you in finding the right place and type of exercise programme so that you will enjoy it more. One of my own research studies with fitness groups suggested that female classes are enjoyed for reasons of social contact and tension release, while male classes showed preferences for health and fitness motives. You tend to find that many male classes involve vigorous 'circuit training' movements with an emphasis on self-monitoring of performance. Women, on the other hand, usually participate in more dance-related classes. However, whatever the nature of the class, it should fit in with your *motives for being there*. One of the reasons for people quitting a programme is that their motives are not satisfied. For example, you go to enjoy yourself and meet other people, but then find that the exercise class is too 'serious' and has no 'group spirit'. Consequently, you 'drop out' and maybe seek an alternative activity.

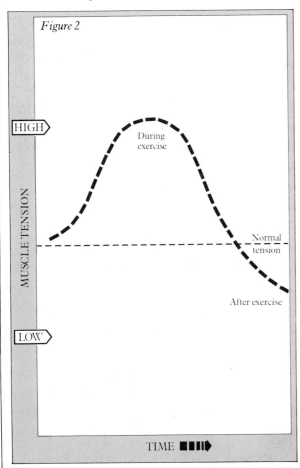

Figure 2

HIGH

During exercise

Normal tension

After exercise

LOW

MUSCLE TENSION

TIME

Health beliefs

In the 1960s and 1970s there was a concerted effort, particularly in the USA, to find out why some people were able to motivate themselves to do something about their own health (such as take the advice of a doctor), while others failed to carry out a prescribed programme. After many studies investigating such diverse areas as diet control, pill-taking, visits to doctors and clinics, attending special check-ups etc., these psychologists started to develop a model of 'health beliefs'. In other words, they were able to identify the major reasons why people did, or did not, take action in regard to their own health. In summary, they said that in order for people to take action:

1 They need to possess minimal levels of health knowledge.
2 They need to have some feelings of being vulnerable to ill-health.
3 They need to view a condition (such as heart disease) as threatening.
4 They need to be convinced of the benefits of taking any action.
5 They need to see few barriers in their way.

Of course, this is over-simplified and there are other factors that contribute to a more complete picture, but these have been found to be the major 'health beliefs' that influence behaviour. So what has this got to do with lifting weights? It is possible to extend this research and look at people who do, or do not, take action with respect to physical exercise. The original 'health belief model', given above, is mainly concerned with ill-health rather than positive health, such as exercise. It may, however, give us indications as to why some people may take up exercise. Research I have done with a colleague at North Staffordshire Polytechnic suggests that some of these factors are very important in being able to distinguish between exercisers and non-exercisers. Changing people's beliefs, therefore, may influence participation rates in exercise, including using weights. Related to this is the major issue of staying with an exercise programme: the problem of exercise 'adherence'.

Exercise adherence

If I really had '*The answer*' as to how to motivate you to start and maintain an exercise programme, I would have sold the idea and retired by now! However, whilst there are no easy answers, there are some simple guidelines and strategies that may help. First of all we need to identify the problem. It is known that well over half the number of people who start an exercise programme quit within a few months. Although some of the factors contributing to this are physical (for example, many 'drop-outs' are over-fat compared with those who stay with a programme), most factors are psychological in nature, many of which are open to change.

Starting a weights programme

To get started, it is best to find an exercise partner. You are much more likely to keep going, especially at times when you are really not too enthusiastic, if a partner is there to encourage you. The second strategy you can operate is to draw up an exercise timetable for you and your partner. This is shown in Exercise 2. You may also want to write in a 'positive statement' next to the timetable. This should make you feel like lifting weights when you read it; for example, 'weights make me *fit* not fat!' (*see* Box 2).

By having this timetable you are more likely to organize your day to accommodate the weights session. It is best if the session is at the same time and place since this allows you to think of that time as 'weights time' and nothing else. To say "I will fit it in when I can" is a fatal strategy – it will never get done. Try and think of times and places that are convenient and accessible. This is not always easy when relying on special clubs or leisure centres for equipment, but it is worth bearing in mind. Home exercise equipment is becoming cheaper and may be an attractive option for those people who find it difficult to get away from the home to work-out.

Maintaining involvement

Now that you have made a start, how do you keep it going? You need to look at two main factors: *you* and *your surroundings*. Let us take *you*, first. If you are one of those individuals lucky enough to be highly self-motivated to lift weights, then you will need little help. However, many people find that they would like to continue their programme of exercises but really cannot find the motivation. Box 3 has been designed specifically with this problem in mind.

Other strategies that may help here could include operating the 'work before play' principle. In other words, set yourself the target of working out with weights *before* you indulge in any personal treat or reward. You should also have clearly stated and measurable goals set for yourself, such as completing three hours lifting

BOX 2
STARTING A WEIGHTS PROGRAMME
Personal timetable and positive statement

Your timetable

	am	pm	eve
Monday			
Tuesday			
Wednesday			
Thursday			
Friday			
Saturday			
Sunday			

Positive statement

" ....

.... "

Notes

1 Shade in an area on the timetable when you intend to lift weights.
2 Try and schedule convenient times.
3 Do this with your exercise partner.
4 Write in a positive statement which makes you feel good about lifting weights!

and can easily see improvements (good for motivation) or slumps (which are then identified for correction). In terms of your surroundings, you should check the following two factors:

1 Your general lifestyle.
2 The place where you lift weights.

Look at your lifestyle: how active is it? Does your lifestyle help or hinder the chances of you exercising? Do the people around you, such as your family, support your efforts to exercise? If they do not, then you need to try and get them on your side since this will greatly help your chances of staying with a programme. For instance, perhaps husband/wife/flatmate would share the babysitting/household chores to give you the free time you need for weight-training.

By looking at the place you lift weights you need to consider how accessible and convenient the facilities are. If your local weights facility is very inconvenient, clearly it will not help you in your quest. If money is a problem (and some gyms are expensive), check with your local council for the nearest subsidized gym. Perhaps alternative methods may be better, such as going to a different facility, even if not quite as good, or exercising with weights at home. Barriers to participation can be highly significant factors in whether we participate or not. A study in the USA found that the university staff members who attended a voluntary exercise class at lunchtimes tended to have their offices near to the gymnasium! Try and remove these sorts of barriers by locating convenient facilities.

We often start out on new ventures with a great deal of enthusiasm, only to see this wane and disappear. This is the 'New Year resolution syndrome'! To be fair to ourselves we are not likely to be able to stick at anything that is suddenly thrust at us in this way. It requires too much of a 'shake-up' in our lives. In fact, it may be better to start off with one session a week and build up to two or three sessions a week, rather than throwing ourselves in at the deep end. So in summary, we need to make *gradual* and *comfortable* changes to our lives in order to accommodate weight-training, or indeed any other form of exercise. You are setting unrealistic goals to expect success otherwise.

Finding reasons for your exercise behaviour
As a final comment on motivation, it is important

per week throughout this month. (*See* Box 3 for further details on goal-setting.) Coupled with this is self-monitoring. Here you would keep a record of indicators of participation, such as the number of sessions and amount of time spent in the gym (training!), and also a record of the body measurements you wish to change. Measure yourself weekly with a tape measure, remembering that changes will be gradual. (For best results, you need to train at least three times a week.) Do not weigh yourself more than once a fortnight, or you will be disappointed: body weight fluctuates daily, and a more gradual assessment is needed. By recording these or, better still, drawing graphs, you keep a record of your involvement to consider the way in which we appraise our own health and fitness. Your motivation to continue this form of exercising will largely depend on whether you think that you can bring about the changes you desire. Consider the following characters and their motives:

Fateful Frank: now 'fateful Frank' is the sort of person who feels that 'what will be, will be'. He feels that he cannot really influence the state of his own health and he was born rather 'big-boned', anyway. All this weight-training will do nothing for his shape... he thinks. Now statements and thoughts like these will only lead Frank into trouble. He has attributed his over-large size to stable factors beyond his control, and hence he is unlikely to try to do anything about them.

Doris the doer: now 'good old Doris' feels that she is in control of her own destiny. For example, she feels that she really could do something about her shape through using weights. She is likely to be more motivated to exercise since she can 'see a way out' of her problem. She has attributed her size to controllable factors that she can do something about.

In essence, *try* and see a way *forwards*. Negative self-statements dwelling on the unchangeable aspects of yourself will do little to help.

The final word

As a final parting shot, it is worth recalling the nature of this chapter. In writing a section on the psychology of lifting weights, I have considered the minds of the 'heavy' lifters: psyching-up, self-confidence, beliefs, etc. There are many weight-trainers now developing mental training pro-grammes to go alongside the more usual physical training packages. Secondly, I spoke about health psychology; how people have found positive links between physique, self and 'body attitudes' and other psychological factors. Finally, the old problem of motivation reared its head. There are simple strategies that can help; you are referred to Boxes 2 and 3. Whatever your own personal motives for lifting weights, or for reading this book, you can be assured that there will be plenty of satisfaction to be derived from an involvement in the lifting of weights. At the end of the day, whatever the physical changes are that accompany weight-training, it will be your own psychological perceptions of those changes that will eventually determine whether you continue as a weight-trainer and find it satisfying.

BOX 3

MAINTAINING A WEIGHTS PROGRAMME

Stage 1: Identify your exercise problems

Write in the boxes below, in column one, things that seem to give you problems with respect to weight-training sessions, eg, 'not enough time in the day'; 'the exercises seem boring'. Then in column two, write in alternative strategies which could help overcome these problems. For example, if your spouse is resistant to the idea of your weight-training, sit down with both your list of reasons for and against, and see if you can work out a compromise; or if the exercises seem boring, write out five different programmes with as much variety as possible. Finally, in column three, give each alternative a rating out of ten marks for the probability of actually putting the alternative into practice. If it is highly likely that you will use the alternative strategy, give it a high mark out of ten, say eight or nine. Now start your weights programme again, but this time attempting the alternative strategy with the highest number.

Exercise problems	Alternatives	Rating out of ten

Stage 2: Set a target

To help your motivation, set a target which is:
★ close in time
★ realistic, but not *too* easy
★ clear and measurable

Write in the next boxes your targets and how you are going to set about achieving them. In column one, write in your targets, using the guidelines above; and in column two, list your proposed actions. List a minimum of two clear targets for the next two weeks.

Targets	My action

Stage 3: Reward yourself

Reward yourself for achieving your targets. If you do not quite make it, reappraise the targets and, maybe, give yourself a small reward for getting close! Keep the rewards in per-spective, however, as you are lifting weights because you *want* to, not because of personal bribery!

PROFILE:
SHABNAM CHAUDHRI
WEIGHT-TRAINING TO HELP PUT ON WEIGHT

Weight-Training to Put on Weight

Shabnam Chaudhri, 21, is manageress of an East London Menswear shop. The shop is ninety-feet-long and, with only mirrors to help her, she prides herself on being able to spot and then outrun the shoplifters that often plague the shop. Her willingness to put herself on the line could stem from a dream she holds: to be selected as a Metropolitan Police Officer. When she applied to the Harrow Road Selection Centre in June of 1985, she was rejected at the preliminary interview because she was underweight for her height (Shabnam, 1.68m/5ft 6in tall, was then 43kg/7st). The selection board told her that she would be reconsidered if she could gain a stone in weight.

Shabnam wondered what she should do. Exercise seemed a good idea – something that would make her fitter, but she was not sure what sort to choose. When she confided her problem to a customer in the shop, he recommended a good weight-training gym in the area. Shabnam's boss was a weight-trainer as well, and he encouraged her to have a look. So in July of 1985, she went along to Dianne Bennett's 'Bodyworks' gym in Forest Gate, East London. Dianne knew that Shabnam wanted to add bulk, *not* muscle mass, so she helped her devise two separate weight-training programmes: one for general fitness, and one for Shabnam's specific needs. Shabnam had five sessions of a general programme to get used to training with weights before embarking on her own special programme. She now attends the gym twice a week, alternating the two programmes. She prefers using the free weights to working with machines, and this is reflected in her special programme, which is outlined below. (*Note:* She rests for half a minute between each set, and for two minutes after each pair of exercises is completed.)

The leg section
1 & 2 Sit-ups (on a slant board) and leg raises (on the floor): three sets of ten reps each.
3 & 4 Squats with a barbell (using 88kg), and pullovers on a bench (using 55kg): for three sets of 15 reps each. She asks someone to hand her the barbell and then watch while she performs the pullovers.
5 & 6 Calf raises on a board (using 110kg), and leg curls on a machine (using 66kg): for three sets of 20 reps each.
7 Leg extensions on a machine (using 55kg): for three sets of 20 reps.
8 Lunges with a barbell (using 44kg): for four sets of ten reps.
9 Heavy squats, using the calf raise machine with the shoulder rolls lowered: she performs two sets of ten reps using 88kg, and two sets of ten reps using 176kg.

The chest section
10 & 11 Bench press (using 66kg), and dumb-bell flyes using 4kg: three sets of ten reps each.
12 Pectoral deck machine (using 77kg): for four sets of 20 reps.

The shoulder section
13 & 14 Press behind the neck using a barbell, seated. Shabnam could not remember what weights she used on this. A friend hands her the barbell from behind, and she does three sets of ten reps. This is quickly followed with front and side dumb-bell lifts, again using the 4kg dumb-bells, for three sets of 16 reps.

The back section
15 Bent-over rowing: using 44kg on a barbell for four sets of ten reps.
16 Lat pull-downs behind the neck, using 66kg: this exercise is performed on a lat machine for three sets of ten reps.

The waist section

17 Waist twists: she either uses the waist twist machine or sits astride a bench with a light barbell behind her neck, and twists from side to side, for four sets of ten reps to each side.

The whole routine takes one hour and twenty minutes, which she follows with a quick shower and a sauna for ten to fifteen minutes. She then goes home for her evening meal.

Just as important now to Shabnam as her exercise regime is her diet: out went all the junk food she loved to eat, and in came wholemeal bread and a concentration on protein and wholesome carbohydrate foods. A typical day's meals for Shabnam might be: an egg and two pieces of toast for breakfast; four brown rolls with tuna at 11.00am; a piece of fish and a roll for lunch; and a meat and potato curry for dinner. She also snacks on bananas and tangerines, and often makes a fruit salad of apple, banana and orange covered with condensed milk. She eats this at work, and says that her workmates are sick of the sight of it! She allows herself one treat a week: a bar of chocolate and a packet of crisps. Apart from all this, she takes a protein supplement in milk twice a day.

Shabnam did not notice any results from her weight-training programme for over a month. Then her friends began commenting that her legs had 'filled out'. Between July and November 1985, she put on over a stone in weight. She now weighs in at 52.5kg/8st 4lbs, and although she still looks slim, she never thinks of herself as 'skinny' any more. She has added a shapelier muscle tone to her frame, and plans to keep on weight-training to keep in shape, even though her ideal weight goal has been reached. Now if she chases a shoplifter, she feels she could 'have a go' if this were called for. Before, all she could do when she caught up with one was to say, "If you do not come back with me willingly, then I will be obliged to use force". Luckily for Shabnam, they always came with her! ("If they had tried physical force *then*", Shabnam admits, "they would have knocked me over.")

Shabnam has found Arnold Schwarzenneger's book *Education of a Body-Builder* very helpful: it enabled her to get more out of her exercises by reinforcing correct technique. "Before, I was bending my knees on calf raises, and not feeling much effect", she says. "Now I keep my legs straight and really feel it." After a trip to visit her native Pakistan in January of 1986, she intends to reapply to the Metropolitan Police Force. When she first started weight-training, her main motivation was to stay the course for three months in order to win a £10.00 bet from a friend. Now she weight-trains for her *own* reasons, with fitness, strength and endurance her top priorities. She has even started to enjoy her regular training sessions in the gym – they have become a routine part of her lifestyle.

Shabnam wanted to build up her body size and put on weight in a controlled way when she started weight-training – now, she trains to maintain her fitness.

CHAPTER FIVE

SYSTEMS AND EQUIPMENT

by Bob Hills and George Green

Weight-training used to be undertaken with free weights only; namely, dumb-bells and barbells. Nowadays there are a whole range of machines to exercise muscle groups in the same way that free weights do. Both machines and free weights have their advantages and drawbacks, but can be seen to complement each other: dumb-bells allow greater flexibility in a range of movement; barbells offer more control and weight; whereas machines steady the movement, add a degree of safety, and often reach muscles that free weights cannot reach. A good weight-training programme incorporates both free weights and machines.

In a single chapter such as this, we cannot hope to do any more than give a brief overview of the thinking and principles behind the main types of weight-training equipment. Until such time as a comprehensive 'Consumer Guide' to weight-training systems and equipment becomes available, this section will attempt to outline the main features of most of the equipment marketed.

Muscles and Activity

Muscles retain and increase their efficiency (a combination of strength and stamina) through activity. Anyone who has had a long enforced stay in bed will know how quickly this efficiency is lost. Weight-training is an efficient and physiologically sound method of ensuring that activity takes place and, further, can be used to ensure that certain desirable features can be encouraged and the undesirable limited. The various systems and machines described here all represent different ways of trying to increase the efficiency of the activity itself, ie, in terms of getting a maximum return for the time, money, effort and other factors spent in exercising.

At its simplest, weight-training involves using a muscle or group of muscles against a resistance, represented by a weight. The greater the resistance/weight, the greater the muscular effort needed to move it. (However, isometric exercises present some exceptions to the comments in this section.) The mechanics of muscular movement present a problem for the weight-trainer and the equipment manufacturer alike. Muscles tend to be thicker at their centre and thinner at either end, where they are attached to the bones. The effort that can be exerted is directly proportional to the amount of muscle available. Thus, if a resistance or weight is moved through the *whole range* of the muscle's movement, then the effort or strength is not even or consistent throughout. This is known as the 'Strength Curve.' If the amount of strength available through a muscular movement is plotted on a graph, it starts off low, at the point of fullest extension, increases rapidly towards the middle of the movement, and then drops off again towards the end of the movement. At the start of the movement and at its finish, the muscle will have greater difficulty moving the weight than in the middle, where a larger amount of muscle fibre can be brought to bear on it. As a result, the weight-trainer is placed in a quandary. Either he or she must choose a weight with which the lower ends of the Strength Curve can cope, and thus not work the centre of the muscle as effectively; or use a heavier weight, which will be correct for the most powerful part of the muscle but will give the trainer great trouble at the beginning and end of the movement. Thus, in body-building particularly, but also in all forms of weight-training, any idea of training at a particular percentage of one's maximum is complicated by the fact that the maximum varies at different parts of the movement. The different systems and equipment discussed in this chapter represent different ways of approaching this problem.

Free Weights

Until comparatively recently, free weights, with their associations with circus strongmen, were what weight-training was all about. Free weights are basically dumb-bells and barbells. Dumb-bells are smaller, designed to be held in one hand, and most exercises using them do so in pairs. A weight is attached to either end of a metal bar, either by spot-welding or with a screw through a sleeve which enables the weight to be varied. Dumb-bells range from the very basic, right up to highly-polished, chrome-plated, machine-tooled beauties, but basically they are all the same. Barbells are longer versions of them, with a bar sufficiently long to allow both hands to grip and with extra room at the ends for the adding of more weight. Some barbells have a succession of angled 'kinks' where the hands grip, in order to allow the muscles to be worked at different angles.

Dumb-bells and barbells are frequently interchangeable, each having their particular advantages and emphases for various exercises. Dumb-bells generally allow the weight-trainer greater flexibility in his range and angle of movement, whereas barbells give more control and weight, so that weight-trainers usually use both to complement each other.

As will be shown later on in this section, the movements of limbs and muscles involved in performing machine exercise essentially duplicate those involved when exercising the same area with free weights. However, while the machines have drawbacks, they do overcome the two main problems associated with free weights. First, although the number of exercises that can be performed is large, free weights can be limited in application, and a machine will sometimes be able to exercise a body part that free weights cannot. (The reverse, of course, is also true.) Secondly, when using free weights, the weight-trainer must at all times be in absolute control of his movements, both for reasons of safety and to ensure that the desired muscles are being exercised in the correct way. A machine steadies the movement, and thus the weight-trainer may concentrate upon the effort of overcoming the resistance. As long as the machine provides the exact effect that the weight-trainer is seeking, then this is ideal. However, sometimes the greater flexibility

Dumb-bells and barbells are metal rods of varied lengths, onto which weighted plates are added at both ends: some allow you to change the poundage (through screws and metal collars), while others are fixed. They range from the basic to the machine-tooled.

of free weights can be an advantage, and the usual answer is to use both free weights and machines, and take the best from both.

To begin with, free weights are usually taken to include a limited number of other items of equipment. Even the most puritan of gyms will probably have a bench, a leg press, an abdominals board and possibly a leg extension/curl machine, as well as perhaps a Preacher Curl bench. (Some of these pieces of equipment will be discussed in the cable/chain/lever section.)

The bench

The bench is an invaluable aid, providing support for all sorts of exercises, as well as enabling the weight-trainer to do exercises both sitting down and prone. The hinge at one end allows the bench to become a chair, supporting the back, and the supporting piece may be adjusted to several different positions from vertical to horizontal.

The abdominals board

As the name suggests, this board is predominantly for exercising the muscles at the front of the torso. It may be placed at several different angles, hooking onto bars fixed to the wall at intervals. At the top end are twin pads, which provide a hold for the feet. As well as exercising the abdominals, the board may be used for exercises in which the body is in an inverted position.

Chin bar

The hands grip the bar, and pull the body up until the chin touches it. You have just lifted twelve stone! It can be used also for hanging, and doing various leg raises.

Preacher bench

Also known as a Preacher Curl, this can be used only for one exercise, and thus many gyms prefer to use the incline bench for this exercise and keep the extra space for other equipment.

Commercial Systems and Machinery

In dealing with the above, we have categorized –

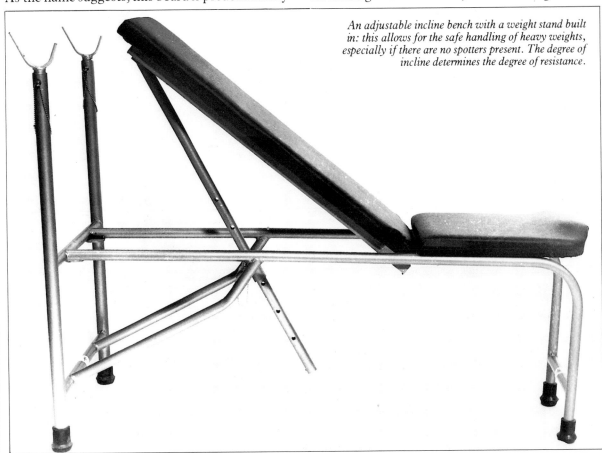

An adjustable incline bench with a weight stand built in: this allows for the safe handling of heavy weights, especially if there are no spotters present. The degree of incline determines the degree of resistance.

as far as possible – according to type, rather than taking each make of weight-training equipment individually. Also, our categorization is necessarily not absolute – as, for example, some cam-type machines also feature cables and/or chains. What we have done is to try and categorize according to the single most *important* characteristic, and proceeded to discuss the various makes under those headings. Our selection is, we hope, wide, but does not attempt to be comprehensive, and it should not be assumed that if a particular type or make is not mentioned that this implies any form of value judgement. All machines perform their functions; it is frequently up to the preference of the individual weight-trainer which one best suits his/her style, needs and physique.

This is a 'multi-station', which allows four or more exercises to take place around its frame. The addition of pulleys and bars makes it even more versatile. It is fixed to the floor, making it safe as well as space-saving.

This section will try to guide and illuminate, and to explain the various principles by which different machines operate. The categories we have used are:

1 Cable or chain and lever type.
2 Cam type.
3 Hydraulic type.
4 Schnell.

1 Cable or chain and lever type
This type of machinery relies on the operation of pulleys for its effect. The resistance is provided by

weights arranged in a stack, which can be added to by the insertion of a fixing pin or other device below the desired weight. A cable or chain is attached to the top of the stack, and runs over a number of pulleys before finishing in a bar which the weight-trainer grips and pulls on, thus lifting the weight with his/her effort.

The individual arrangements of cables and pulleys are known as stations, and can often be used for more than one exercise. They can be acquired in single flat units which attach to a wall and occupy little space (the *Powersport* Module) which, although obviously limited in application, are very useful. At the other end of the price, complexity and space ranges are the multi-station gyms, which can feature a large number of stations, all fixed around a square frame, which concentrate a large and varied number of exercises into considerably less floor space than would be occupied by the same number of individual machines.

It should be noted that even with the most comprehensive of multi-station machines, it is still necessary to have a few extra machines for specific exercises, and most manufacturers make a selection of dual-purpose machines to supplement the multi-stations. They also make various combinations of smaller multi-station machines – which one would best suit an individual or a given gym would very much depend on their particular requirements. As mentioned in the free weights section, most gyms will include a leg press machine, and probably a dual-function leg machine. Free weights are not really adaptable enough to perform a full range of leg exercises in safety. So it will probably be necessary for a gym of this type to have a multi-station gym of a chosen type, one or two separate leg machines, and a selection of free weights.

It will be noted, following the discussion earlier regarding the 'Strength Curve', that the mechanism described here does not make any allowance for stronger and weaker points through the range of movement. This is also true of those stations that use a lever to allow the weight-trainer to move the weight. Thus, although this method is extremely space-efficient and has good general application, it is inherently self-limiting. In recognition of this, manufacturers have made some modifications to their more complicated models. For instance, Multigym (*Powersport*) add a 'roller' mechanism to the stations using the lever method. (This has no application to pulley operated stations.) As the weight is moved, the roller moves along the length of the lever, increasing the resistance. This more nearly corresponds to the Strength Curve and muscular ability, but it is still only a partial answer. *Powersport* call this 'Automatic Variable Resistance'. *Peak Fitness* call it 'Independent Variable Resistance', and achieve the effect by the use of a drag mechanism on the pulley stations, which increases the resistance as the lift or pull develops. They also make dual-purpose machines and small

This is a seated 'lat' machine operated by a cable, bar, and a weight stack, and it exercises the 'latissimus dorsi' muscles of the upper back.

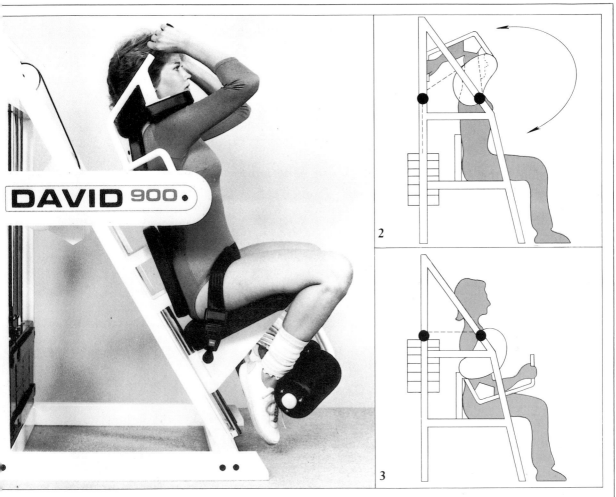

multi-stations. *Universal* make a wide range of every type of omni- to multi-station, using the plain pulley and lever methods. *Atlanta* machinery uses the same principle, but the machines are designed to be used in a larger area, and are specific rather than multi-purpose.

2 Cam type

The Cam System represents a different answer to the problem of the Strength Curve. The principle has been applied in a number of different designs and applications, but the basic principle is as follows: the weight stack both resembles and is adjusted similarly to the Cable and Pulley machines. From the stack runs a chain or cable, which is fixed to one end of a shaped cam. The bar that the weight-trainer pushes or pulls is fixed by the same method to the other end of the cam. Instead of the cable running over a freely-turning flywheel, as in the pulley machines, where the cable is merely guided, the cam itself dictates the path of the arc of movement into an ellipse rather than a circle. It is easier for the weight-trainer to

1 A cam-operated machine that exercises the abdominal muscles: the user bends forward from the waist, creating abdominal contraction. 2 A cam machine used for the bent-arm pull-over exercise. 3 The completed arm movement shows the cam can extend movement to as much as 240°.

begin and end the movement than it is to go through the central 'longer' part of the movement. Consequently, although the weight remains the same, the resistance increases throughout the movement until a certain point is reached, and then decreases. This will immediately be seen to be a more exact representation of the path followed by the Strength Curve, and is in this way a more satisfactory arrangement. This means both that the weaker parts of the muscle are not over-stressed, and that the stronger part gets a full work-out. This is obviously more efficient in terms of both time and effort.

There are a number of systems which use the cam principle. Perhaps the best known are *Nautilus*, whose machines are predominantly omni- or duo-functional. Consequently, they are usually to be found in larger gyms. They are highly specific, and there is a comprehensive range of possible exercises, though the full range would be expensive and take up a lot of space. *PowerCam* supplement the range of *Powersport* pulley-operated machinery with a cam-based series, which uses the same principle and has its advantages, but which loses the advantage of size. Unlike *Nautilus*, this range is not intended to be comprehensive. *David* also use the Cam principle, and are perhaps the most aesthetically pleasing of this type, as well as having a very smooth action, whereas *Polaris* are perhaps the remaining best-known make in this category.

As we have already suggested, it is difficult if not impossible to lay down the law about the various makes of machine which use similar principles and designs. Consequently we suggest that the prospective weight-trainer try as many as possible for himself, and choose the one he finds most attuned to his own needs and feelings.

3 Hydraulic type

This type of machine has no cables, chains or weights. Instead, when the weight-trainer exerts a force upon the bar or lever, resistance is provided by a hydraulic valve. As the exertion takes place, the motion pushes a plunger through a tube, forcing liquid through a valve. The size of the valve can be regulated, in order to give a greater or lesser resistance.

This presents a slightly different set of options to the cam-type machine. Instead of the resistance being pre-set and following a pre-determined curve dictated by the machine, this type of machine allows the weight-trainer to dictate his own resistance, not only at the points at which significant alterations take place along the Strength Curve, but at any point during the lift or pull. Given that the weight-trainer exerts himself at a consistent level, then the degree of resistance will be the same percentage of his muscular maximum, for as his strength increases through the movement, so will the resistance to his exertion. As the machine only resists an exertion, and is not dependent on gravity, this means that if

the weight-trainer takes on too much, then he is not committed to it, for he may always push less hard, which decreases the resistance. The other advantage is that, like the Nautilus type of cam machine, one is working maximally throughout the movement; but *unlike* the cam-type, one works through *both* movements. Muscles work in pairs: for example, to extend and flex the arm. When working against a weight-stack resistance, the weight-trainer works to lift it, and then could just let go to return it to its former position. Hydraulic machines, however, once pulled or pushed, have to be pushed or pulled back into position, so both of the sets of muscles are exercised on the same machine, almost simultaneously.

The principal benefits of this are two-fold: first, there is obviously a most significant time-saving element; and, secondly, as one is working constantly throughout, there is a high aerobic demand, which lends this type of machine to a very intense form of training. It does rely heavily on the weight-trainer being sufficiently highly

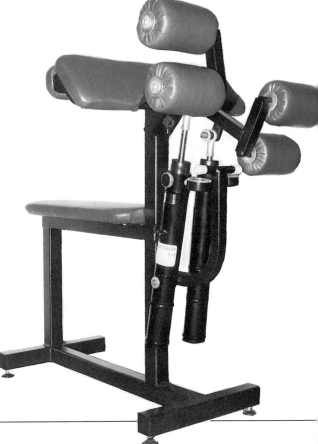

The Hydra fitness *biceps/triceps machine. It has no cables, chains or weights; when force is exerted on a bar or lever, resistance is provided by a hydraulic valve.*

A leg stretch exercise on a Body Ess *machine, which uses air-compression pistons as its power source. The pistons are built into two power packs. The pulley ropes are added to the basic frame.*

motivated to push or pull as hard as possible at all times, which is less of a problem with other systems, where either a weight is lifted or it is not. The main manufacturer of this particular type of equipment is *Hydra Fitness*.

Body Ess

Body Ess deserves a special mention of its own, although it actually falls into the hydraulic category of weight-training equipment. It is a new type of equipment that is sold primarily for use in the home, but it is also used in hospitals and rehabilitation centres. It uses air-compression pistons as its power source, instead of springs or weights. The pistons are built into two power packs, which can be placed in three different positions on a basic stainless steel frame. Pulleys connect from either the top or bottom of the frame. A bar in the middle of the frame can be moved up or down, and can be added to with a pulley bar, pulley handles, a lat bar and ankle straps. The power packs can be adjusted for different resistance independently of each other, depending on the exercise; each individual sets the resistance and speed that is suitable for his/her needs, and then sets it with a simple, self-locking pin.

Body Ess trains muscles using variable resis-

Left: leg raises performed on the incline board of a Body Ess *machine for the lower abdominals. It is safer for the back to do this exercise with bent knees (see the 'In and out' exercise, page 56) than it is to lift the legs straight up and down.*

Below: sit-ups for the upper and middle abdominals performed on the incline bench of a Body Ess *machine. Crossing your arms across your chest (or placing fingertips to temples) prevents pulling up from the shoulders and neck.*

tance (the resistance in the power packs adjusts to the differences in muscle strength occurring at various points in a movement), and this is where it differs from other hydraulic equipment. With other hydraulic machines, the resistance needs to be pushed back to the starting point, whereas with *Body Ess*, the weight returns on its own. Variable resistance also means that although the actual weight of the resistance ranges from only 4–48kg/8–96lbs, you can obtain the effect of lifting 100kg/260lbs by doing quicker repetitions which affect the muscle's 'load curve'. This is known as *isokinetic* training, and it is thought to reduce injury from over-training – the only difference is that movement speed (ie, training pace) is decided by the individual and not by a machine. *Body Ess* can be used for muscle development, endurance, improved circulation and flexibility. It offers three programmes: light resistance (for cardiovascular endurance and trimming exercises); medium resistance (for shaping and toning); and heavy resistance (for strength and body development).

Up to 60 substantially different exercises can be devised on *Body Ess*. The equipment works silently, due to the air pistons, and can be assembled in 30 minutes. It is said to be easy to change around for the various exercises. Because it only requires 206×96cm/82×38in of wallspace and weighs only 20kg/45lbs, it is handy for home-training, as long as you do not want to use the equipment for heavy weightlifting – it is really a toning machine only. It comes complete with its

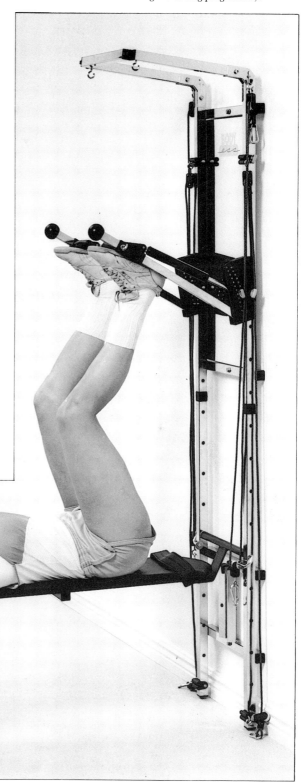

The leg press exercise performed on a Body Ess *machine: the legs push the resistance up and down, and the front upper thigh in particular gets a strong work-out (these muscles are often hard to reach in a normal weight-training programme).*

The shoulder press exercise, which also works the biceps, as performed against the air-compression resistance of a Body Ess machine. This kind of training equipment is ideal for home use because it takes up so little room.

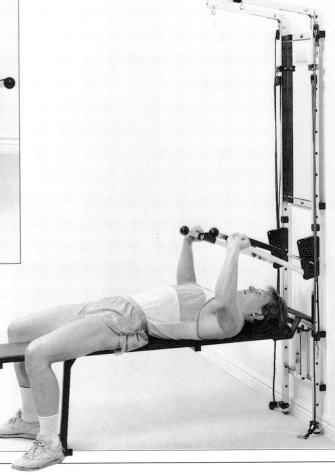

Above: Lat pull-downs to the back, performed on a Body Ess machine. The wide bar is essential in order to give the upper and middle back muscles a proper work-out.

Right: the bench press exercise performed on a Body Ess machine. If you suffer from back trouble perform this exercise with bent legs (with feet on the end of the bench).

own bench, mirror, fitness training guidebook and an exercise wall chart.

4 Schnell

Schnell equipment presents a categorization problem, for it falls to a certain extent within several of the other categories. It is divided in two. The first area is called Synchro-Fitness. This features a 'drive unit', which automatically synchronizes the 'load curve' (the resistance) to the strength curve of the weight-trainer (one might visualize it as an automatic gearbox). Like the hydraulic system and the cam system, this means that a maximum training effect is achieved throughout the movement. Each machine exercises an isolated muscle group through a full range of movement. Each synchro machine has two positions to exercise the two opposed muscles in a specific muscle group: for instance, the arm curl exercises the biceps, whereas the reverse arm curl exercises the triceps. The other part of the system is called Duo-Fitness, which concentrates on muscle groups around *joints* (eg, knee and hip), rather than on the larger groups of muscle. These machines are more simply built, with no chains or cables. However, a fairly large number of machines would be necessary for a comprehensive workout, as the two systems are designed to be used in conjunction. The Duo-Fitness system does not have a drive unit – it uses, among other things, polymide straps – but this is less important, as the Strength Curve applies less to the muscles being worked by them.

Summary

All the above, then, are examples of groups of exercise machines that take a certain principle and then apply it to weight-training. Each has its advantages and its areas of weakness. As we mentioned earlier, there are other systems available, which operate on similar lines, and it would be difficult to choose any one system that was so manifestly superior to any other on the market that we could unreservedly recommend it to the exclusion of all others. The variety of

Above: Schnell leg extension machine. This machine features a drive unit, much like a gearbox, which automatically synchronizes the resistance to the 'strength curve' of the individual trainer. Left: the Schnell 'lying leg curl' machine, again featuring the drive unit. Each 'synchro' machine has two positions to exercise the two opposed muscles in a specific muscle group. Schnell equipment is expensive and new, and found in only a few gyms.

93

weight-training equipment offers you a choice: use the one that suits your needs best.

Other Pieces of Equipment

As well as the machines mentioned at the beginning, which are in some cases not true 'machines' as such (but which obviously fall under the scope of this subject as being useful aids to weight-training), there are a number of other items of equipment that the weight-trainer may use as part of his/her training programme:

Jogging machines are obviously a useful apparatus, particularly in the centre of towns, or when the weather makes outside running an unattractive prospect. They can be used for warming-up, cooling-down, or just to provide the consistent aerobic work that weight-training alone can lack. The basis of all 'joggers' is a belt, rotating around two rollers set at either end of a frame on the floor. The runner stays in one place while the 'ground' moves past beneath him. (This takes a little getting used to.) The running surface usually has some 'give' in it, which makes it a useful alternative for those who do a lot of road-running. The controls are situated within reach, and start with an 'on/off' switch, a 'fast/slow' switch, and a speed, time and distance read-out. Other features may include a gradient increase facility, to simulate hill running. Computers have been attached to joggers, both to give sophisticated monitoring and analysis of the runners' performance as well as to work the controls of the machine. Perhaps the most common joggers are made by *Powersport Engineering*, but there are others, including *Tunturi* and *Universal's* Tredex.

Bouncers are frequently used as an alternative to a jogging machine, or as a complementary method of training. They are a small circular trampoline, upon which one runs. Owing to the rebounding effect, a high degree of aerobic and muscular benefit can be gained, without any of the jarring associated with normal running. They can be used for warm-ups or training, and have some rehabilitative applications, too.

Rowing machines can be acquired separately, although many multi-station gyms have one rowing station. These, however, do not usually give leg-work, but concentrate on the arms and back. The Individual Rowing Machine seats the rower on a sliding seat, and props the feet against a small platform, similar to that found in 'real-life' rowing. The rower then pushes backwards with the legs, while pulling a bar or lever into the chest. The resistance given by the bar or lever can be adjusted, and, as the arms and legs are working together, the legs are also worked harder or easier by the adjustment. This is the machine at its simplest, but it can also be obtained with a computerized read-out – programming digital 'opposition' for the competitively inclined! With the correct technique, and with safety in mind,

A treadmill is the 'cheap and cheerful' version of a jogging machine. It works on a conveyor belt principle, and it can be graded to increase resistance. This one is made by Tunturi.

rowing machines are a useful warm-up exercise, and can be helpful in aerobic terms if used sufficiently long enough; but their main function is to provide a good general work-out for the arms, back and legs. The best-known basic machine is made by *Tunturi*, whereas the computerized version is by *Universal* which also manufactures a much simpler version.

Exercise bicycles are a feature of most gyms, owing to their usefulness as warm-up machines, as well as their easy adaptability for physical assessment purposes and their aerobic usefulness relative to their size. The simplest are little more than two crossed pieces of tubular steel with a seat and pedals; but there are many intermediate bicycles that give good results. One can also use the *State-of-the-Art* models, which give computerized fitness read-outs at the touch of a button. The basic principle is simple. When the cyclist turns the pedals a flywheel is turned, usually in the same place and in the same manner as the front wheel of a normal cycle. Resistance to the pedalling action may be increased by the use of a braking mechanism. This may be effected by direct contact on the flywheel, by tightening a strap running around its circumference, or by a number of more sophisticated methods – but the idea remains the same. The more the resistance increases, the harder the cyclist must pedal in order to maintain his speed. A constant pace is maintained throughout, and thus the pulse-rate will rise. For assessment purposes, this gives a good idea of the cyclist's stage of fitness, while for training purposes a good aerobic training effect is ensured. By this pulse-monitoring it is relatively simple to ensure that the cyclist works hard enough, without over-stressing himself.

Bicycles may thus be used as warm-up and warm-down aids, as well as part of an integrated fitness training programme. The very simple bikes are not really useful for more than the most basic training, but there are several in the medium-price-and-complexity range that give good results, and where the read-out and calibration are accurate enough to allow the cyclist to work out workload, aerobic capacity and calorie burn-up. The best known mid-range machines are perhaps the *Tunturi* Ergometer and those made by *BodyGuard*, while *Universal* also make both the ordinary type as well as the 'LiveCycle' and the 'Aerobicycle', which are as close to pedalling a computer as you can get.

A jogging machine powered by electricity moves the belt underneath you. This machine is at the expensive end of the price range, and 'extras' such as speed, time and distance read-outs are included.

Heavyhands Equipment

Finally, a word about *Heavyhands*, which fit functionally into the category of weight-training, albeit slightly uneasily. They are, as the name suggests, light weights designed to be held in the hand, but with a double grip, so that the weights do not need to be gripped tightly. Rather than performing what might be regarded as a weight-training exercise *proper*, the user follows a programme of calisthenics, or does a normal aerobics or body conditioning class holding the heavyhands. The extra effort involved in performing arm movements while holding the extra weight increases the quality of the work performed by much of the upper body muscles, as well as increasing the aerobic potential of the exercises. The *Heavyhands* may also be used in normal jogging, where added work and aerobic benefit may be gained by involving the arms more in the work done by the body, as well as the normal amount of work done by the legs. Ankle weights can also be obtained, which make the leg muscles work even harder, thus giving greater aerobic effect.

Male and Female Weight-Trainers

When weight-trainers are spoken about it is common to use the term 'he' to cover both men and women – this is not to imply that weight-trainers are solely, or even primarily, men! Although there are a minority of exercises that women should avoid or adapt, the fundamental principles governing the physiology of men and women, and the benefits gained from this form of training, are exactly the same. Owing to the larger amount of testosterone in the male physique, the male will tend to grow in size, depending on the amount of weight used and the exercises performed, whereas the female will tend not to grow, but will gain tone, suppleness and definition as well as strength. Weight-training for women is increasing in popularity and rightly so, for it no more makes a woman lose her femininity than it can guarantee a man's masculinity. It is an efficient, physiologically sound way of getting the body you want, whatever one's sex, and any other connotations are superfluous.

Finally, a word to the wise: weight-training is a great way of getting the Body Beautiful and keeping it that way. However, like any sport, it has its hazards, which, as in other sports, can be minimized with common sense and a professional approach. So, always take advice before attempting anything, and always play safe. Better to walk and get there in the end with no problems than to run and end up with a frustrating injury which means having to start again at the beginning. First and foremost, enjoy your training.

You can work-out on an exercise bike at home or in the gym (opposite). All the machines shown here (left and below) will help tone up muscles and make you firmer and stronger. But wherever you work-out, make sure that you bear the safety guidelines in mind and do not exert yourself beyond your ideal training level.

PROFILE:
JUDY OAKES
WEIGHT~TRAINING FOR A SPORT

Judy Oakes was 27 years old in 1985, the year she became Britain's top female shot-putter. In 1972, Judy was being coached by Otto Feldmanis, who suggested that she take up weight-training in order to improve her style. At first, Judy had to be dragged into the gym. "I was terrified of what it would do to my body shape", she admits. Although she soon settled into a routine of two 45-minute sessions a week and had learned all the lifts, she was not taking it very seriously. It was not until 1974, when Mike Winch became her coach, that her attitude changed.

Mike, who has been one of Britain's top male shot-putters for over a decade, felt that Judy did not have enough range in her movements, so he re-vamped her whole training programme to enable her to train as hard as a man. The idea was to use weight-training to build muscle mass and create a stronger body to help her shotputting. "A woman's arms and back are normally weaker in comparison with her other body parts", Judy explained, "and these are the particular body areas that are used most in shot-putting." She began doing three half-hour sessions in place of the two 45-minute ones, and worked hard. Her routine included bench work, squats, dead lifts, neck presses, leg and abdominal exercises and lots of dumb-bell work. Apart from this, Mike made sure that she was eating the right protein foods and taking vitamin and mineral supplements. It was not long before Judy was transformed "out of all recognition".

"Before I started", she says, "I was chubby; now I actually weigh more but look slimmer." (This is because muscle is heavier than fat; Judy is 1.64cm/5ft 4½in and 78.5kg/12st 7lbs.) All her hard work paid off: after just one year of training, Judy had added two metres to her throwing distance, and in 1976, she made the British Athletics Team. "The weight-training helped me enormously", she says, "the more weight I could lift, the better I could throw the shotput. It changed me from an average club competitor to a world-class one." That same year, the British Amateur Weightlifting Association held a pilot scheme for a women's power-lifting competition. Mike suggested that Judy should enter – she did, and duly won it. It was then that she decided that she should train for weightlifting competitions during the months of the year that did not conflict with her shot-putting, in order to keep her competitive instinct sharp and her body in shape. Summer and autumn constituted the shotput season, so that left winter and spring to seriously compete in weightlifting.

In 1981 and 1982, she was World Champion Women's Power-lifter, in a competition that included backsquat, bench press and dead-lift. The 'snatch' (taking the weight from the floor straight into the air) and the 'clean and jerk' (taking the weight first to the chest, and then into the air) are events that take place in Olympic Lifting Championships; in the first of its kind held in October 1985 for women, Judy won the 82.5kg class, with a 75kg snatch and a 95kg clean and jerk. Other best performances to date are 207.5kg in the backsquat, 112.5kg in the bench press, and 210kg in the dead-lift.

When training for a power-lifting competition she never trains with the weight she plans to lift – she aims to train at 10 per cent under that figure. She has learned that the adrenalin boost you get in a competitive situation makes up for that missing 10 per cent. The trick is not to push the 'arousal curve' (the point where mind and body meet to give you your best lift) beyond physical control, but rather to strive for a balance between mental excitement and physical control. "When you channel that bit of competitive instinct", she says, "you can always lift more than you think."

Above right: weight-training helps Judy Oakes compete with the shot put. "It changed me from an average club competitor to a world-class one", she says. Below: Judy, showing the style that made her Britain's top female shot-putter in 1985. She trains with a squad of athletes, twice a day, seven days a week.

A week before a competition, Judy starts seriously reviewing all the various alternatives of action in her head. An hour before the competition, she isolates herself from the rest and builds up her concentration: "*Somehow* you have got to make it different from training". Two other things she has to cope with are the fear of losing, and the fear of success – the latter because there are new pressures on you in terms of expectations. Mentally, she works out a plan to cope with either: she finds that *training* in a competitive situation (for example, against men who are given a 70kg handicap) helps her to do this.

In 1982, Judy became self-employed, and she now helps Mike with his gym in Wimbledon between competitions. She also works out in a squad of 10 other athletes, training twice a day, seven days a week: running, jumping, lifting and weight-training. Twelve years after starting weight-training, she is still working out three times a week. Her advice to beginners is to get a trained professional to show you the basics; otherwise, you could do yourself an injury. She herself injured her back in 1980 through poor weightlifting technique, and missed being chosen for the Olympic squad. "Good technique is essential", she says. It did not take long for Judy to get her technique right: in 1984, she was placed fourth in the shotput event at the Los Angeles Olympics.

CHAPTER SIX

WOMEN AND WEIGHTS

by Dianne Bennett and Janice Townson

Up until recently, women were not encouraged to weight-train. It was considered a male domain, and conjured up pictures of huge, sweaty bodies pumping iron in dingy gyms. All sorts of myths arose to keep women away: women would become 'musclebound', lose their attractiveness, become less feminine. Nothing is further from the truth! The female shape and hormones are not conducive to building muscle mass, and unless you are on an intensive body-building programme (including very heavy weights, extra food, and protein supplements) the most you will get is a streamlined body and trim muscle.

Since time began, women have been conditioned generally to view themselves primarily as patented baby machines. Biologically, that is what we are, but progress in social evolution has left us with *other* options. We are now free to choose.

Historically, we have tended to strive for the shape that men have decreed as desirable, *not* the form or silhouette in which we felt comfortable. Up until recently, female fashion, both of clothes and form, has served to accentuate fragility, inhibit mobility and establish the myth of inferior intellect and strength. Can you imagine Chinese women choosing to have their feet bound, or Edwardian women enjoying being lashed into 18-inch corsets, or even American women accepting Howard Hughes' distorted vision of 'perfect' women's breasts?

Now our options are open – we can still choose to force or disguise our bodies into the ideals of others, or let time, neglect, misuse and gravity take their toll naturally. The revelation is that we have *another* alternative: the possibility (within certain biological limits) of creating our *own* body shape by working-out with weights.

Some of you may want to bodybuild (ie. muscle-build) in a serious and competitive way, choosing the challenge to shape and sculpt your body, muscle group by muscle group, reducing your covering of body fat to rock bottom, and displaying your incredible achievements in public contests. However, thousands of others have more mundane aspirations.

Most common is the incentive to use weight-training as a simple but effective body-balancing

tool. We cannot make structural changes, ie. to height, shoulder or pelvic girth, torso or leg length, but we can use our muscles as living, moulding clay to fill out or file down, and create a totally different optical illusion. For instance, you can weight-train to increase shoulder-width to balance and detract from a wide pelvis and 'hippy' look, flatten the 'tum' or define the waist, and lengthen a short torso. There are gluteus movements to tighten and lift the buttocks whilst pulling those jodphur thighs into sleekness; and chest (pectoral) exercises to support and elevate the breasts, irrespective of volume. After working through the beginner's course, and mastering the basic grip, stance and breathing, as well as learning the language of 'reps' and 'sets', it is a simple matter to design a personal schedule for 'taking off' or 'putting on', where you will. The good news is that while your first concern may be the aesthetic rewards, the bonus will come in the form of extra energy, more strength and greater well-being; as well as a greater projection of confidence, enthusiasm and sexuality. It matters little whether you are fourteen or seventy-four – the 'terrific three' (Stamina, Strength and Suppleness) are equally coveted and attainable with an individually-tuned weight-training programme.

You have made the big decision: to train with weights and to be in control of your own body shape. As a total novice, you have yet to distinguish between a dumb-bell and a swingbell, but it is imperative that your initiation into weight-training is pleasurably safe and productive. So whether your final choice is to train with weights

in a plush spa, basic working gym, sports complex, school gym or in a garage with a mate, ensure that you receive the expert tuition to which you are entitled. Every woman today can take responsibility for her own health, strength and bodily well-being, and, as a consequence, enjoy the fruits of her labours.

About Women and Exercise

The myth of the weaker sex has at last been exploded – so let us now eliminate any other misconceptions and misinformation. One myth is that women do not need to exercise if they are not 'sports-minded'. It is important that we exercise to maintain strength and efficient body-functioning for many reasons: for instance, how many womb prolapses and varicose veins, not to mention lengthy labours could have been averted, had muscles remained strong, circulation efficient and stamina levels high?

Another myth is that weight-training will 'give you muscles'. Centuries of fostered ignorance and accepted feminine ideals still leave their mark. Be assured that women do indeed have muscles, exactly like men, but they are disguised by a thicker fat layer due to the female hormones, and provide the curves that are synonymous with womanhood. Increasing the strength and tone of muscles can only improve the functioning of women's bodies and give them a new firmness and shape to their body covering. In fact, it is *just* these hormones and extra fat deposits that make it so arduous for a woman to display muscularity, should she *choose* to train for competition body-building. High-muscle, low-fat ratio do not just happen for females – those that strive towards that goal must have the champion sportsperson's dedication, mental application and superior physical genetics. Most of us fall into the category of generally reluctant athletes, and average keep-fitters who have come to the shattering conclusion that 'if you don't use it, you lose it!' For many women, lack of overall strength, stamina and suppleness have forced them into taking strong measures.

Another statement that needs investigating is "I want to lose (or gain) weight". In the former instance, what exactly is it you want to lose? A woman's body weight is made up of several components including water, bones, organs, muscle and fat, but presumably she is referring to the reduction of fat when she registers a desire to 'lose weight'. Losing fat can be achieved by surgery (if you are wealthy and desperate) *or* by the more sensible act of balancing ingoing and outgoing calories. This forces the body to utilize stored fat. Add exercise to diet and you are on your way to safeguarding lean muscle tissue. *Fat is the only weight we need to lose* – the rest we must retain and protect to ensure good health.

Another misinformed statement often heard is: "Muscle turns to fat when you stop training, doesn't it?" Muscle becoming fat, or fat becoming muscle is a biochemical impossibility as their composition dictates that 'never the twain shall meet' – a real-life 'chalk and cheese' situation. When professional sportspeople decline physically on retirement from their regular strenuous participation, becoming flaccid and paunchy, this is often attributed solely to their inactivity. It is assumed (wrongly) that the rippling muscles of effort have been reduced to the rolling fat of lassitude. It is true that without regular resistance movements the muscles will lose some tone, strength and size, but the superfluous poundage results in ignoring individual calorie needs. If the body is fed identical quantities, no matter what the demands, the calories not required for body functions and energy expenditure will be stored as fat for the possible eventuality of 'lean times' – which for most of us never materialize. We therefore end up building our very own personal, ever-present 'fat mountain'.

Most widespread and fondly cherished of all myths is the 'sweating the weight off' fallacy – *would* that it were true! In fact, the sweating process produces two effects: eliminating waste-products and providing the body with its cooling system, keeping the temperature at 98.4°, by evaporation of sweat on the skin surface. This is very efficient, but it is not liquidized fat oozing through those pores as some imagine – only water. As soon as we take in some fluid this lost water is replaced. We do not assume that we have lost body fat when we eliminate urine or faeces, nor count in ounces or grams the nail clippings or cuttings, dead skin or dandruff that we lose. So to reiterate – the only way to lose fat effectively is to reduce our calorie intake, and then to exercise to firm up the body.

One question often asked is: "What is the ideal weight for my height?" You could well respond – "Are redheads brighter than blondes?" It is back to the whole question of our individuality, genetic factors, ratio of muscle to fat, body proportions and fat distribution. If at 1.68 m/5ft 6in the scale registers 63kg/10st, only visual scrutiny can determine aesthetic perfection, or gross over-loading. A tape stretched at 90cm/36in, can mean many things to many bosoms: perfection of shape and position, or a wide back with mini breasts, or a narrow back with ample breasts. It is impossible to assess ideal 'weight and measurements', as no scale or tape can determine what is 'right' for *you*.

Finally, there seems to be a universal fear of becoming 'muscle-bound' when no one is quite sure what the term implies: a new brand of super-glue, or a physical affliction? The man or woman who is so muscle-bound that mobility is inhibited is yet to be found, so do not worry about 'over-doing it'. It would be almost impossible for you to do so, even if you set your mind to it!

Weight-Training During and After Pregnancy

What are the benefits of exercise/weight-training for the pregnant and post-pregnant woman? They are both mental and physical:

Mental benefits:
1 An increase in self-confidence.
2 An increase in the ability to confront resistance – this provides useful preparation for the hard work of labour.
3 A reduction in the level of stress and tension.

Physical benefits:
1 An improvement in posture.
2 An increase in muscle strength and endurance.
3 An increase in flexibility.
4 An improvement in circulation.
5 An increase in stamina.
6 A shapelier figure which will be regained faster after pregnancy.

7 A corresponding increase in overall fitness which will reduce fatigue and sluggishness.

The following body areas are particularly important during pregnancy:

1 Pelvic floor – a strong pelvic floor will help a pregnant woman to cope with the weight of the baby and with the birth itself. After pregnancy these muscles need to be gently toned. This will also help bladder control.

2 Abdominals and back – both need to be strong in order to support each other, control the posture and help with the birth.

3 Legs – leg exercises may help to prevent varicose veins and cramp. The circulation will be improved, and increased flexibility in this area is useful for the birth process.

4 Arms and shoulders – these areas must be strong in order to carry the baby afterwards.

5 Chest – strong pectoral muscles will support heavy breasts. Interestingly, the relationship between exercise and pregnancy, in terms of positive effects, may be a two-way relationship. For example, Ingrid Kristiansen broke the world marathon record when her son was one and a half years old and feels that she has been a better runner since his birth.

Weight-training and pregnancy

Pregnancy is not the right time to introduce weight-training. Furthermore, it is unnecessary, as the increased body weight provides sufficient resistance for strengthening. A woman who is experienced at weight-training may continue doing so but she should modify her usual training programme and discuss her intentions with a doctor or specialist and check with them throughout her pregnancy. The weights programme should be adapted accordingly. Normal limits should not be extended. See the *Guidelines* section later in this chapter.

Weight-training after pregnancy

When an activity such as weight-training can recommence after the birth of your baby will depend upon fitness levels before, during and after pregnancy. It would be wise not to introduce a weight-training programme until six months has elapsed, by which time your body will probably have fully recovered. However, depending on recovery and preparation, it may be

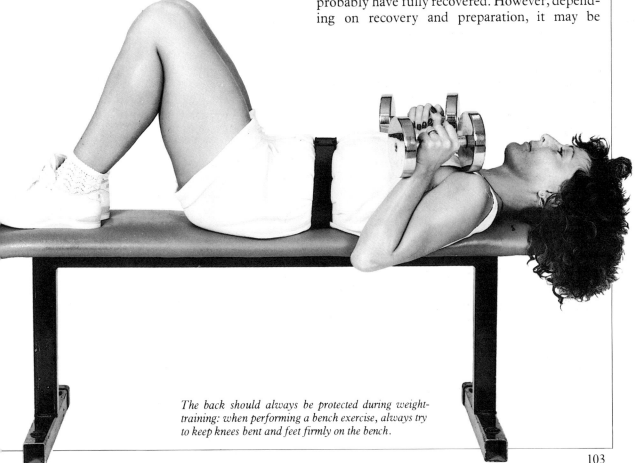

The back should always be protected during weight-training: when performing a bench exercise, always try to keep knees bent and feet firmly on the bench.

possible to commence *before* the end of six months. A doctor's or specialist's approval should be sought. It is a good idea to prepare the body gradually for weight-training by carrying out gentle toning exercises without weights. You can then progress to the use of light ankle and hand weights and finally to a more intensive weight-training programme which can be improved upon gradually. (See Chapter 3, *Beginner's Free Weights Programme*. Also, refer to the *Guidelines* section.)

Other forms of exercise during pregnancy

In general, pregnancy is not the time to introduce *new* forms of exercise, especially if you are unfit and do not exercise regularly. However, provided that there are no medical reasons against it, you may benefit from the introduction of very gentle exercises when pregnant. These refer to con-trolled simple movements which are carried out slowly and methodically and are designed to gradually stretch and strengthen the muscles and joints. These exercises are often yoga-based, emphasizing body awareness and control. Such integration of body and mind prepares a woman for labour. A good example of this is the pelvic floor exercise, described under *Premenstrual* at

the end of this chapter.

Swimming is an excellent activity at this time because it has all the advantages listed earlier and your body weight is fully supported. Provided it is done in a relaxed manner, it may be introduced during pregnancy. It will complement the body control exercises described in this chapter as it has the additional benefit of stamina.

More vigorous forms of exercise, such as tennis, running and aerobics, should *not* be introduced during pregnancy. However, most forms of exercise need not be harmful if a woman normally does them. For example, the long-

Please note the hand position in the photograph: it is very important to keep the thumbs facing up. Also, do not grip the heavyhands weight too tightly. As you gain strength, you can add more weight.

Pump and walk

1 *Stand upright with weights on hands; bend right knee and raise right hand to* waist *level, keeping left arm straight.*
2 *Return right hand and knee to a straight position. Now bend left knee and raise left hand to* waist *level; then straighten them. Alternate from right to left for ten reps.* **3** *Now bend right knee and take right hand up to* shoulder *level; return them both to a straight position and repeat to the left side. Alternate sides for ten reps.* **4** *Now bend right knee and raise right hand above your* head; *return them both to a straight position and repeat the movement to the left side. Alternate sides for ten reps. Perform this exercise smoothly, as if you were walking in place. In all three hand positions, work up to 20 reps maximum.*

1   2   3   4

Floor exercises (stomach)

1 Lie on your back with weighted hands, arms by your side. Flex feet and bend knees into chest. 2 Stretch legs to the ceiling, keeping your bottom on the floor. Bend knees as before, then straighten legs back down to the floor. Do 20 reps maximum.

1 Lie flat on floor, holding weights above head. Sit up and inhale, bringing upper body off the floor and stretching arms to ceiling. 2 Exhale as you stretch forward with feet flexed. Return to start, inhaling. Do 20 reps maximum.

1   2   1   2

Heavyhands guidelines

1 Work only to your maximum. You can gradually extend yourself as the weeks go by.
2 Heavyhands will not build muscle, but it will sculpture your body to show the muscle shape.
3 Heavyhands is a complete body-conditioning programme which works the cardiovascular system.
4 As long as you listen to your body and do not overdo your Heavyhands training, it is a safe, easy way of getting fit.
5 Using Heavyhands regularly will give you strength and endurance to participate in other sports.
6 Be prepared to work many muscle groups. Your torso, especially, may feel as though it has really been worked in the first week or so. Persevere and soon you will feel the benefits as your body grows stronger, especially in the stomach and back.

Spine stretch: *1 Start with legs apart and your weighted hands held straight above your head; inhale. 2 Keeping your legs apart, swing your upper body through your legs, exhaling. Return to start position and do 10 reps.*

1   2

any exercise or sport during pregnancy, whichever one you choose.

distance runner may proceed relatively uninterrupted by pregnancy provided that she feels well and accepts that this is not the time to set records or achieve new goals. Activities involving the risk of falls or blows such as horse-riding, are not as suitable as, say, walking, swimming, yoga or cycling. It is important to check with a doctor or specialist before commencing or continuing with

Other forms of exercise after pregnancy

Shortly after birth the uterus starts to contract and is likely to be back to its normal size within six weeks. This process will be further stimulated by breast-feeding. Muscles will return to their normal functions at different rates. The gentle strengthening and stretching exercises mentioned will help this process over the first six months.

This type of exercise can continue indefinitely in its own right, but also provides excellent preparation for, and a complement to, weight-training. (It is difficult, for example, to isolate the muscles of the pelvic floor using weights.)

As a general guideline it is wise not to introduce sport or vigorous activity until approximately six months after pregnancy, by which time the body will probably have fully recovered. However, depending upon the level of fitness during pregnancy, and on whether it has been maintained, swimming and cycling (which avoid stress on the pelvic floor), yoga and walking (in flat shoes with good posture) may often be introduced before the end of six months. Again it is important to check with your doctor or a specialist before commencing exercise after pregnancy.

The guidelines for exercise during and after pregnancy

1 Body awareness is crucial. It is important for the mind to listen to the body and take heed of any messages to slow down. Exercise should be enjoyable and should never hurt. Decisions on how much exercise a pregnant or post-pregnant woman should do often depend on how she feels. Fortunately, both pregnancy and exercise tend to 'heighten' body awareness and this should be actively encouraged during and after pregnancy. If in doubt consult your doctor or a specialist.

2 It is a good idea to work according to the principle of achieving less and experiencing more. Quality should take priority over quantity on difficult exercises. During and after pregnancy, the muscles and ligaments are weak, so it is particularly important not to over-stretch them. This is even more important in the case of a very flexible woman as she may become too flexible and develop back problems. A pregnant woman is twice as likely to develop back pain as a non-pregnant woman. This is because the spinal ligaments are softened at the very time when they have to support the greater weight of the abdominals. If possible, it is a good idea to exercise in front of a mirror so that posture and technique can be corrected at all times. Extra care of the spine should be taken for up to nine months after pregnancy.

3 Similarly, different women should expect to progress with exercise at different rates. The intensity and frequency of a programme will depend upon fitness levels before, during and after pregnancy and upon the type of delivery. It is better to do a little and often in order to avoid fatigue than to try to do too much too soon.

4 Rest and relaxation are just as important as exercise during pregnancy. At least two hours' rest, with the body weight off the feet, should be taken each day. Rest and relaxation remain particularly important for the first three months after the delivery. It is unwise to exercise when fatigued or unwell. Fortunately, an increase in body awareness helps a pregnant woman to know whether she is experiencing feelings of genuine tiredness or laziness.

5 Antenatal and post-natal classes can provide excellent advice on healthcare, nutrition, emotional changes, relaxation and exercise techniques. Correct technique is crucial to a pregnant or post-pregnant woman and does not become any less so in the case of gentle stretching and strengthening exercises. It is often difficult to master the control involved in such subtle exercises, and classes provide careful supervision and group support.

6 Exercises should be moderated to suit the pregnant woman in question and her stage of pregnancy. For example, a simple side bend can be carried out whilst standing with feet placed slightly wider than hip-width apart and knees bent; or while sitting on a bench/chair; or seated on the floor. During the latter stages of pregnancy, exercises that entail lying on the back may become uncomfortable, as in this position the enlarged uterus rests on the vena cava, the main vein returning blood to the heart. In this case, pelvic floor exercises could perhaps be done standing with the feet a little wider than hip-width apart and the knees slightly bent. Any alternative position must be stable.

7 It is important not to hold the breath or over-breathe out when pregnant or after pregnancy. If in doubt about breathing techniques, just breathe naturally.

8 General guidelines on clothing, when best to eat before exercise, etc, should also be followed. Wear something loose and comfortable, and *never* exercise immediately after eating.

1

2

Prenatal shape-up exercises

Side leg raise (hip and outer thigh)
1 Lying on your side, start with the toes of the top leg pointing downwards. **2** Concentrating on the hip and outer thigh muscles, slowly pull the leg upwards, keeping the toes downwards. Lower the leg until it almost touches the bottom leg. Repeat. Avoid swinging the leg, or raising it with the toes pointed upwards. Do reps on each leg; working up to 5 reps.

Kneeling squat (thigh and buttock)
1 Start in a kneeling position, with your arms straight out in front of you. **2** Then slowly lower the buttocks towards the floor, keeping your body straight to avoid knee stress. Return to start position. Continue the up and down movement. Work up to 10 reps.

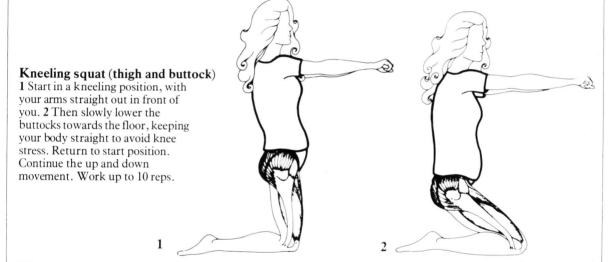

1

2

1

2

Side leg lift (inner thigh)
1 Lie on your right side with the left knee bent and tucked behind the right leg, and the left foot flat on the floor. **2** Isolate the inner thigh muscle by pulling the right leg upwards in an even-paced movement. Keep the side of the foot up. Slowly lower the right leg until it almost touches the floor. Repeat. Do not swing or jerk the leg up quickly. Do 5 reps for each leg.

9 Medical advice should be taken before commencing or continuing an exercise programme.

During and after pregnancy it is particularly unwise to do weight-training exercises that include:

1 The raising of both legs whilst lying on the floor or on an incline board. This is not a good abdominal exercise as it puts a great deal of strain on the lower back.

2 Any kind of sit-up with straight legs for the same reason as above.

3 Squats in which the lowest position of the squat is lower than the position in which the thighs are parallel to the floor. This can put too much pressure on the knee joints.

4 Bouncing movements: these are also stressful to the knee joints.

5 Changing the force of gravity quickly when pregnant. Light-headedness or even dizziness may result because of the large uterus pressing on the vena cava and preventing full circulation for a moment.

6 Isometric exercises: these involve muscles being contracted without any movements of the parts of the body carrying out the contractions. Such exercises are not advisable in that a pregnant woman who may already have higher blood pressure than normal, may raise her blood pressure further.

7 Pushing weight above the head while standing; for example, the standing shoulder press featured on page 57. It is better to do such an exercise seated when pregnant to avoid arching of the back.

8 Lifting a weight whilst lying on the back as the pregnancy develops, for the reasons given under *Guidelines*, no.6. For example, the bench press featured on page 53.

9 Exercises on a leg press machine. This equipment is not featured in this book.

10 Hyper-extensions, particularly of the spine. All arching of the back must be avoided as pregnancy will arch the spine considerably, anyway.

Remember that medical approval should be sought during or after pregnancy before continuing or commencing a weight-training programme.

The following is an example of a programme which could be given to a woman who has fully recovered from the birth of her baby after six months or more. It requires a certain amount of preparation as discussed under *Other forms of exercise after pregnancy*. The woman in question should first be physically assessed and a programme created by a qualified fitness instructor or specialist to meet her overall needs and *not* just the fact that she has had a baby. Therefore, the programme should be balanced. Technique should be taught first *without* weights.

Most of the following exercises are described and photographed in Chapter 3. In practice, the choice of exercises will depend on the equipment available; it is often possible to do the same exercise using fixed apparatus or free weights.

Check your pulse here – at no point should it rise above 85 per cent of maximum heart rate.

Warm-down

(1) Five minutes on the bicycle. Speed 60 RPM. Resistance set in order to to bring pulse down below 100 beats per minute.
(2) Stretches – to be done slowly:

(i) **Cat stretch** (for the spine)
Kneel on all fours on a mat. Hands should be placed directly under shoulders with the feet directly under the hips. Breathing out, round up the back, taking the chin to the chest. Breathe in as you return to a flat back position. Repeat five times.

(ii) **Stomach stretch**
Lie on your back with arms outstretched (and holding on to two dumb-bells in order to help keep the shoulders down) with knees into the chest. Breathing out, lower both knees to one side of the body turning the head in the opposite

(iii) **Groin stretch**
Sit on a mat with the soles of the feet together at a comfortable distance away from the body. Place the hands on the outside of the ankles, with the elbows outside the knees. Breathing out gently, round the back and lower the head towards the ankles. Breathe in as the effort is released. Repeat five times.

Abdominal curl (stomach and sides)

1 Lie on your back with knees bent and feet flat on the floor, arms relaxed alongside you. **2** Slowly curl up; lift only your head and shoulder blades off the floor. Slowly lower to starting position. Use your ams if necessary, but avoid jerking up quickly. Do 5 reps; work up to 10 reps.

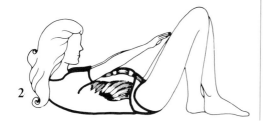

Pelvic rock (buttocks and stomach)

1 Start on your hands and knees, with the lower back and stomach relaxed towards the floor. **2** Contract the stomach and buttock muscles, pulling the pelvis forwards and rounding the back. Then relax. Repeat. Do 5-10 reps.

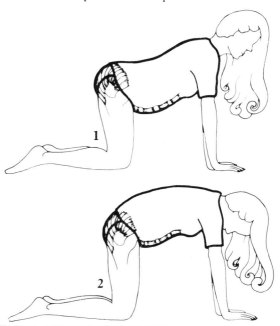

Knee lift (hip and outer thigh)

1 Start on your hands and knees. **2** Pull one leg up laterally to the side, using the hip and outer thigh muscles. Avoid swinging the leg out of control. Lower to start position. Repeat for 4 reps, then switch legs.

Back arch (low back and buttocks)

1 Lie on your back, arms extended out to the side, with knees bent and feet flat on the floor. **2** Slowly raise hips and lower back upwards until the back is in a straight line. Avoid over-arching. Try to tighten the buttocks as the hips are eased upwards. Do 3-6 reps.

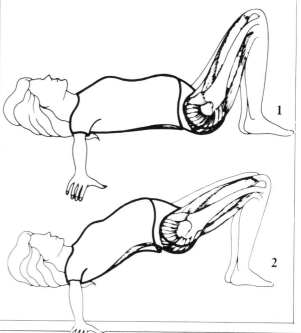

©Bruce Algra 1985. Courtesy ISLM, England.

(iv) Calf stretch

Stand facing a wall with both forearms placed vertically on the wall. Step back with one leg, keeping the other leg forward and bent. Place the back heel on the floor and push down through the heel. Both feet should be parallel to the wall and the hips square on to the wall (*Note*: the pelvis should be tucked under). Breathe out as the weight is pushed down through the back heel and inhale as the effort is released. Repeat on the opposite leg. Hold the stretch for as long as possible on each leg.

(v) Shoulder stretch

Sitting on a mat in a cross-legged position or on the edge of a bench, raise one arm up over the shoulder as far down the back as possible. Breathe out on the stretch and in on the release. The other arm can be used to assist. Do not arch the back. Repeat with the opposite arm. Hold the stretch for as long as possible.

As a guideline, the above programme could be repeated twice per week.

Note 1 – posture

Stand with your feet slightly wider than hip-width apart, toes turned slightly outwards and spread, and weight balanced evenly on both feet. Pull up through the legs, buttocks, abdominals and rib cage. Tilt the pelvis under and pull the abdominals gently in to support the spine. Drop your shoulders and lengthen your neck.

Note 2 – split squats (for buttocks and thighs)

First practise without dumb-bells. Lunge forward so that the front leg bends until almost parallel with the floor; the front foot should face directly forward and the front knee should be placed over the centre of the foot and in line with it. The knee should not over-extend the foot below it. The back leg should be straight with the knee held high. The back toes should face the front heel (although it may be turned out slightly if balance is a problem), which will have lifted off the floor. The arms hang by the side holding the dumb-bells tightly. Straighten the front leg maintaining the posture. This constitutes one repetition. Breathe in on the bend, and out on the stretch.

Note 3 – Curl downs on decline (for abdominal strength and spinal control)

Place the abdominal board on a decline. If this is not possible, leave it flat on the floor. Hook the feet under the foot-grip and sit tall with bent knees. Hold the arms out straight ahead with palms down and shoulders dropped. Very slowly curl down the spine into the board, one vertebra at a time. Breathing out, gently pull in the abdominals, curling the spine off the board in the opposite order until an upright position is reached. The contraction of the abdominals must effect the lifting; *not* a jerk from the back. If this is not possible, do not curl down as low. Breathe in on the way down and out on the way up.

Weight-Training for the Underweight

Provided that a woman is just a little underweight and not suffering from a disease or too weak to train, a weight-training programme can help her to gain muscle and, therefore, weight. In order to build muscle it is necessary to keep the weight relatively high and the repetitions relatively low. Such a programme necessitates a certain level of fitness at the beginning. Although there are no specific exercises, it is important that the programme is carefully balanced to develop muscle in the correct proportions.

Weight-Training for the Overweight

Similarly, a weight-training programme can help an overweight woman provided that she is not suffering from a disease causing the condition, and is not so overweight as to make weight-training dangerous. Again, she must be fit enough to cope with a programme. In this case the emphasis would be on muscle endurance, and correspondingly the weights should be kept relatively low and the repetitions relatively high. The programme should be combined with some form of aerobic exercise, such as walking, jogging, running, cycling or swimming, in order to promote weight loss. The advantage of weight-training here is more likely to be one of keeping the muscles toned and promoting a feeling of well-being.

Note: Both the significantly overweight and underweight should seek approval from their doctor before commencing an exercise programme.

Rear leg pull (buttock and back of thigh)

1 Start on your hands and knees, and slowly pull one leg up towards your stomach. **2** Extend the leg slowly, pulling it back and outwards. Return to start; repeat. Try to feel the lower part of buttocks tighten as the leg is extended; do not kick. Do 3 to 4 reps, each leg.

Side bends (sides)

1 Stand with feet slightly wider than shoulder-width, with left arm up and right arm hanging down. Slowly pull left arm over head and to side, while pulling right arm across stomach. **2** Repeat to right side. Five reps each side and work up to 10.

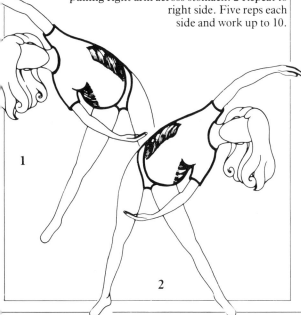

Premenstrual

For many women, exercise helps to alleviate premenstrual tension and stomach cramps. Menstruation may affect ability but this is more likely to be due to psychological and emotional factors rather than to physical ones. The following exercises may help to alleviate cramps:

1 Pelvic floor exercises

Lie on your back, on the floor, with the knees bent and the feet hip-width apart. The knees should be in line with the feet, the arms relaxed by the sides, and the neck and spine lengthened. Keeping your back on the floor, breathe out and contract the muscles of the pelvic floor, drawing them up and in. Breathe in and relax. Repeat several times.

2 Buttock squeezes

In the same starting position breathe out as the buttocks are squeezed so that they lift off the floor. At the same time pull the abdominals gently in and push the lower back into the floor.

3 Curl downs

See *Example of a weight programme*

Menopausal

Exercise is just as necessary during the menopause, especially if the body has been allowed to deteriorate throughout years of inactivity. The psychological benefits of exercise may be just as relevant; for example, tension control. No specific exercises are required, but if exercise is to commence after a sedentary lifestyle, it should be very gentle initially, and then built up gradually as fitness increases.

Post-operative

This cannot be discussed in general terms. Post-operative exercise depends upon the fitness level of the women before the operation, the type of operation and its side effects. Medical advice must be sought before attempting any exercise programme.

Disabled

There is no reason why a disabled person should not weight-train if they so wish, as the benefits gained from strengthening weak muscles is so great. Make sure, however, that you get medical advice before you start.

©Bruce Algra 1985. Courtesy ISLM, England.

CHAPTER SEVEN

GET FIT FOR SPORT

by David Bromfield

Weight-training can be used to achieve a higher level of fitness and endurance in a chosen sport. Sports fall into four broad classifications: 'power and explosive movement' sports, stamina and endurance' sports, 'flexibility and agility' sports, and 'hand/eye co-ordination' sports. Each group of sports calls for a certain kind of muscular exertion and movement – with this knowledge, sportsmen and women can construct a weight-training regime that will enhance their performance in their particular sport. In this chapter, we discuss examples of sports from each group and the weight-training programme that would best suit each of them.

We have all got general ideas about how to get fit for our particular sport. We all know how much better we feel when we have a certain element of fitness, and how much easier our day-to-day activities become. Things like running for the bus, tying our shoe-laces and reaching for the book on the top shelf become infinitely more comfortable to perform when we feel 'fit'. We also know how difficult these things may appear to be when we are not 'fit'.

We have probably all tried jogging at some time or other and done most of the basic 'non-equipment' exercise, too – exercises like press-ups, touch-toes, star jumps and bunny hops. All these activities are fine in their own way and, properly directed, will build a level of basic fitness into our bodies.

However, what we are looking for in this chapter is a more specific angle on how we can get fit for our particular sport and also what useful classifications the various sports fall into. Many sportsmen and women have discovered that regular weight-training can help them to compete better in their chosen field.

Before we develop this theme, let us examine an area of training which is enjoying its most popular period at the moment. This includes Body Conditioning and Aerobic classes which, far from being simply another way of getting fit, have to many people become a sport on their own – providing, as they do in the more reputable centres, companionship and a certain level of self-competition within the structure of a carefully thought-out series of exercises usually performed

to music. These classes typically last for an hour and, in the case of Body Conditioning, usually commence with a 5-10 minute warm-up period which will loosen and warm-up the whole body. This prepares you for the more rigorous exercises to follow, which are designed to shape, tone and firm the body. The exercises will encompass all the major body parts and place the emphasis more on flexibility than stamina.

'Aerobics', on the other hand, is designed to improve and exercise the 'cardiovascular' system.. This is achieved by a warm-up period followed by a 10-15 minute session of more violent exercises performed on the jog. This in turn is followed by excercises similar to those performed in 'Body Conditioning'. The aim of this type of exercise is to increase the pulse rate to a particular level and then to slowly reduce it to almost the starting level by the end of the class. If this type of exercise is continued on a regular basis the participant will achieve a useful level of fitness and stamina and would even begin to lose some body weight.

The final extension of this type of exercise is

Opposite: Aerobic exercise is designed to improve fitness and stamina by exercising the cardiovascular system (top). 'Heavy-hands' is an aid to aerobic exercise: 1 Stand with feet shoulder-width apart, a 'Heavyhand' (1kg/2lb) weight in each hand, arms bent. Inhale. 2 Bend knees and tilt your torso forwards (with flat back); then swing the weights behind you in a pumping action. 3 As you progress, bend your torso even further forward with arms straight up behind. 4 Swing the weights through to the front, lifting arms straight up over head. The four steps together make up one rep. Repeat for 10 reps.

1 2 3 4

'Heavyhands'. This is a development of the 'Aerobic' theme but tends to be more demanding, as hand-weights are carried during the exercise. It has the effect of bringing the upper body more into play, thus developing a more 'whole-body' exercise pattern. It is also an offshoot of Progressive Resistance Training as the hand-weights are adjustable and can be increased as the level of fitness rises.

Choosing the venue

As in the case of choosing a gymnasium for weight-training, the choice of exercise centre for hand weights or aerobics is also very important. Always choose a class that teaches a recognized method and is taught by a teacher qualified in that method. Avoid very large classes as they preclude any individual attention from the teacher. Make sure that the actual exercise area is well ventilated and has a suitable floor, and that floor mats are available. A studio that has lots of mirrors and wall bars is especially beneficial.

Classification of Sports

We can now move on to the broader classification of sports. Most sporting activities fall into four basic categories, and these are:

1 Power and explosive movement sports

Into this category fall the lifting sports, the combat sports, the throwing sports, and sports where sprinting over short distances is required. Obviously within this classification the accent is more on muscular development and strength, and devotees of these sports will already be utilizing the benefits of weight-training in their programmes of fitness.

2 Stamina and endurance sports

These include activities like long-distance running and swimming, cycling and protracted running, and ball games like rugby, soccer, squash and tennis. Participants in these types of

Below: Swimming is a good 'stamina and endurance' sport; while sprinting (opposite) is more explosive.

sport will spend much of their training time performing and practising the particular activity concerned, but will undoubtedly benefit from the added advantages that strictly-applied forms of weight-training will bring to their overall fitness. In these sports it is less advantageous to build muscle mass, so lighter weights will be the order of the day.

3 Flexibility and agility sports
Into this classification fall the sports that require a high degree of agility and body control. These include diving, gymnastics, high-jumping and some of the martial arts. It is vital for the participants in these activities that their bodies are tuned to react exactly when and how required, as many of the movements used require rehearsal and absolute timing. Weight-training, for these people, provides a way of isolating particular muscles required for their activities in a way that more general forms of training cannot do.

4 Hand/eye co-ordination sports
Into this category fall sports like golf, cricket, tennis, badminton, archery and shooting. Many of these sports require a basic aptitude for their performance, or progress within their confines will be limited. For instance, anybody can learn to play *at* golf, but as any weekend hacker will tell you, it is a 'different kettle of fish' to play golf well. In this type of sport there is often one specific part of the body that requires a lot of attention, and weight-training is the ideal medium for isolating and improving it.

Obviously all of these broad classifications overlap into each other to a greater or lesser extent: for example, a tennis player requires a high level of hand/eye co-ordination in order to time the ball well. However, no matter how proficient he or she may be at actually striking the ball, it will not result in any significant improvement unless a basic level of fitness is also present. Therefore two levels of training are required – one to satisfy and improve the mechanics of shot-mak-

Different sports demand a certain level of fitness and expertise.
1 Running requires stamina. 2 Football needs explosive movements and endurance. 3 Gymnastics require agility and body control.
4 and 5 Tennis and golf require good hand/eye co-ordination.

5

ing, and one to ensure that the player is able to be in the correct place to make the shot.

As this book does not set out to be a general sports instruction manual, it will restrict itself to suggesting and planning a training programme to ensure that the body is prepared for the chosen sport, and leave the actual mechanism of the sport to other publications. To this end sports within the four classifications will be discussed showing the different applications of working out with weights with suggested programmes.

Weight-Training Schedules for Popular Sports

There now follows five example of sports with their relevant weight-training regimes. As they do not fall into any specific category, they will be listed numerically:

1 Football
This sport serves to illustrate very clearly how

The short sprints and upward jumps involved in football need the muscle power that weight-training can give.

different activities overlap into more than one of the four classifications. In this instance, there are elements of three of the broad classifications inherent in playing football (soccer). First, there is the need for power and short explosive movements. This manifests itself in the need for short, sharp sprints and upward jumps. Also, there is a need for stamina and endurance, as the game is played over a protracted period with very few stoppages. Soccer also requires a reasonable amount of co-ordination, as the game is centred around a moving ball.

Bearing these factors in mind, here is a suggested programme of weight-training which would prepare a participant for soccer-playing when taken alongside the more traditional methods of fitness training. This programme is to be carried out two to three times per week, but never on consecutive days.

Abdominals
Bent-leg sit-ups: for 3 sets of 20 reps. (see page 56).
In and out: for 3 sets of 20 reps. (see page 56).

Back
Lat pull-downs: to the front: for 4 sets of 10 reps. (see page 56).

Shoulders
Standing shoulder press: for 3 sets of 10 reps. (see page 57).

Chest
Flat chest press: for 4 sets of 10 reps. (see page 57).

Legs
Thigh extensions: for 4 sets of 10 reps. (see page 58).
Leg Curls: for 4 sets of 5 reps. (see page 61).
Hack squats: for 4 sets of 10 reps. (see page 64).

As you can see from the programme, an all-body regime to tone up all the main muscle groups is required, while giving particular attention to the legs and stomach areas where the 'kicking' muscles are found. It is stressed again that this programme is designed to augment the normal type of football training that most competitive players take part in.

2 Golf

This is a sport, unlike football, that would not, typically, have strong links with weight-training – or any real training apart from practising the actual game itself (most people are able to walk a golf course). However, as has been demonstrated by some of the modern champions, physical fitness and strength are increasingly playing a greater part of the preparation for the golfer. Although golf falls mainly into our fourth category, there are elements of flexibility, power and stamina required in order to play this game to a decent standard. A programme of exercises is suggested here that should be undertaken twice a week, but not on consecutive days.

Abdominals
In and out: for 3 sets of 20 reps. (see page 56).

Back
Lat pull-downs to the front for 3 sets of 10 reps. (see page 56).

Shoulders
Upright row: for 3 sets of 10 reps. (see page 62).

Chest
Dumb-bell pull-overs: for 3 sets of 10 reps. (see page 63).

Arms
Triceps push-downs: for 3 sets of 10 reps. (see page 60).
Biceps curls (with reverse grip, ie. palms down): for 3 sets of 10 reps. (see page 58).
Wrist curls: for 3 sets of 10 reps. (see page 54).

Legs
Thigh extension: for 4 sets of 10 reps. (see page 58).
Leg curls: for 4 sets of 5 reps. (see page 61).

As can be seen from the pattern of exercise suggested, the predominant muscles in a golfer's armoury are the hitting muscles: the triceps, the forearms, and the wrists, which each have an exercise of their own. The legs are also included, which give power to the stance and the swing. The better prepared these muscles are, then the more likely that the player can retain rhythm and consistency right to the end of the round, and the more power he can generate to lengthen his game without the need to overswing.

3 Racquet sports (tennis, squash etc)
As previously mentioned, tennis, and to a similar

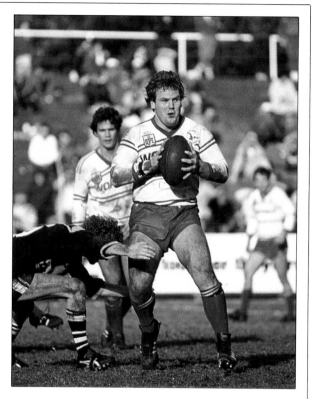

Rugby is a 'stamina and endurance' sport. Weight-training can help participants by increasing overall fitness.

degree, squash, fall into three of our basic categories, whilst being primarily a hand/eye co-ordination sport. The main difference between 'light-racquet' games like squash and badminton, and 'heavy racquet' games like tennis, is that the former are played with a flexible wrist and the latter with the whole arm, ie. with the wrist locked. However, for this discussion it is more or less immaterial, as the strength required in the wrist to keep it locked is the same as is needed to play a game with more 'wristy' movements.

In tennis even greater control is now required by the modern, heavy 'top-spin' game, as the racquet hits upwards in a brushing movement rather than merely through the ball as before. Here then is a suggested training programme to be carried out ideally three times per week with at least one day in between sessions.

Abdominals
Crunches: for 3 sets of 20 reps. (see page 62).
Roman chair sit-ups: for 3 sets of 20 reps. (see page 59).

Back
Lat pull-downs to the back: for 4 sets of 10 reps. (see page 62).

Shoulders
Shrugs: for 4 sets of 10 reps. (see page 60).

Chest
Seated chest press: for 4 sets of 10 reps. (see page 59).

Arms
Overhead cable triceps extension: for 4 sets of 10 reps. (see page 64).
Biceps curls: for 4 sets of 10 reps. (see page 58).
Wrist curls: for 4 sets of 20 reps. (see page 54).

Legs
Hack squats: for 4 sets of 10 reps. (see page 64).
Calf raises: for 4 sets of 10 reps. (see page 61).

The predominant muscles used in this type of sport are those of the stomach, the legs and the arms, especially the wrists and forearms.

4 Athletic field events (throwing)
Obviously we must consider the throwing field events separately from the jumping ones, since different muscle groups and techniques are employed. It is no coincidence that in almost every case throwers have the largest muscle mass as compared to other athletic team members. While a high degree of technique is involved in Shot-Putting, Javelin, Discus-Throwing and the Hammer event, much of an athlete's training for these events is taken up with the development of power and strength.

Any suggested training programme will almost certainly be used to augment programmes already in use. No doubt the competitor will already be familiar with weight-training, and may already have devised a programme based on his or her own preferences. Here is just such a suggested programme which should be used on alternate days, with a three-day rest after each three-session cycle to avoid muscle strain.

Abdominals
Bent leg sit-ups: for 4 sets of 20 reps. (see page 56).
In and out: for 4 sets of 20 reps. (see page 56).

Back
Seated pulley rows: for 4 sets of 10 reps. (see page 59).
Lat pull-downs to the front: for 4 sets of 10 reps. (see page 56).

Water skiing, like snow skiing, requires strong thighs and upper arms. Strong shoulders are a 'must'.

Shoulders
Shrugs: for 4 sets of 10 reps. (see page 60).
Standing shoulder press: for 4 sets of 10 reps. (see page 57).

Chest
Flat chest press: for 4 sets of 10 reps. (see page 57).
Seated chest press or dumb-bell flyes: for 4 sets of 10 reps. (see pages 59 and 63).
Dumb-bell pull-overs: for 4 sets of 10 reps. (see page 63).

Arms
Overhead cable triceps extension: for 4 sets of 10 reps. (see page 64).
Triceps push-downs: for 4 sets of 10 reps. (see page 60).
Biceps curls: for 4 sets of 10 reps. (see page 58).
Wrist curls: for 4 sets of 10 reps. (see page 54).

As you will note, this is very much a 'whole-body' regime with particular emphasis on the chest, upper arms and legs. Wherever possible, movements have been chosen that require the limbs to work through a greater range of movement in order to preserve muscular flexibility. Shrugs are very important to an aspiring thrower, as they move the shoulders through a full rotation.

5 Water and snow skiing

These two sports are closely linked despite the total difference in the environments in which they are performed. The requirement is still for strong thighs and upper arms. The shoulders also need above-average strength as, especially in the case of water-skiing, a locked position must be held for some time. It is vital that a degree of flexibility is attained since both mediums, snow and water, are far from regular. As these particular sports are expensive, it is vital that the aspirant does not lack fitness at the outset, as this can increase the time needed for improvement in what is often only a short availability period. Build up first to a useful level of basic fitness, and augment this with the following weight-training programme:

Abdominals
Crunches: for 5 sets of 20 reps. (see page 62).
In and out: for 5 sets of 20 reps. (see page 56).

Back
Seated pulley rows: for 4 sets of 10 reps. (see page 59).

Shoulders
Shrugs: for 4 sets of 10 reps. (see page 60).
Upright rows: for 4 sets of 10 reps. (see page 62).
Standing shoulder press: for 4 sets of 10 reps. (see page 57).

Chest
Dumb-bell flyes: for 4 sets of 10 reps. (see page 63).

Legs
Thigh extensions: for 5 sets of 10 reps. (see page 58)
Leg curls: for 5 sets of 5 reps. (see page 61).
Calf raises: for 5 sets of 10 reps. (see page 61).

Arms
Triceps push-downs: for 5 sets of 10 reps. (see page 60).
Overhead cable triceps extension: for 3 sets of 10 reps. (see page 64).

Squash is a 'light-racquet' game, requiring a strong but flexible wrist: weight-train for strength, power, flexibility.

Standing biceps curls: for 5 sets of 10 reps. (see page 58).

These movements will emphasize the areas in which maximum power is required and will serve to condition the whole body.

Summary

What has been attempted here is to single out some individual sports and suggest suitable weight-training regimes to enable participants to perform at a more satisfying level. It is obviously not feasible to list every sport here as this would become repetitive and involve a great deal of overlap. However, the examples given have been chosen so that recognition by other sportsmen of areas that overlap or run parallel will be sufficient to allow them to piece together their own programme, and to recognize the similarities in their sport to those mentioned.

Sports generally are a huge area of human interest and any book can only hope to *touch* on areas of usefulness. It is up to the individual, armed with the basic information and advice given here, to actively seek the best means of attaining the level to which he aspires. Good luck!

CHAPTER EIGHT

WEIGHT~TRAINING TO RECOVER FROM INJURY

by Rose Macdonald

It is not well known that weight-training is more than just a fitness activity: it is also used to help injured athletes and sportspeople recover from injury more quickly. Injured muscles are weakened, and weight-training strengthens the muscle up to its previous healthy state. Physiotherapists use weight-training as part of their rehabilitation programme: it is not something that can be undertaken by an injured sportsperson on his/her own; he or she must be carefully supervised, and weight-training can only be introduced when the injured muscle is ready to accept it. A trained physiotherapist knows when this stage has been reached.

Rehabilitation of the Sportsman

Physiotherapy and rehabilitation of the sportsman are a little different from that of the non-sportsman. The sportsman has the pressures of training and competition to deal with and he is anxious to get back to training as soon as possible. It is most important that fitness be maintained while the injury is being treated.

Initially, a careful assessment is made of the injury, and a detailed history is taken. If an athlete or sportsman has incurred the injury, certain things are noted: the level of competition, the nature of the sport, the date of the next competition, the stage of training the person is at, his/her training load, etc. It is important to be aware of all these details as they give an idea of the psychological stress the patient is undergoing. The first question asked by the injured person is

usually "How soon can I play?" – and he would like this to be 'yesterday!'

Here is a rough guide to the length of time that various tissues take to heal after injury:–

Skin: 2–3 weeks
Muscle: 4–6 weeks
Tendon: 6–8 weeks
Ligament: 6–8 weeks
Bone: 12–16 weeks
Nerve: 12–18 months

These figures are not hard and fast and can be influenced by a number of factors:

1 By minimizing secondary complications, healing and repair time can be *decreased*.
2 If critical care is delayed or inappropriate, recovery time can be *increased*.
3 Activity too soon after injury will delay healing and repair, and may result in a permanent functional disability.

Rehabilitation of the injured sportsman is the most important aspect of treatment, because the degree of rehabilitation often determines his/her ability to safely and effectively return to competition. Inadequate rehabilitation predisposes the injured person to re-injury and may restrict any future participation in sport. It is most important to maintain a high level of fitness while an injury is healing. This will ensure that less time and effort

Rule of thumb

For every week an athlete has been away from activity due to injury, it will take approximately one week of rehabilitation. This is assuming that he is on a well-designed programme. Failure to rehabilitate an area after injury increases the danger of further damage on your return to sport.

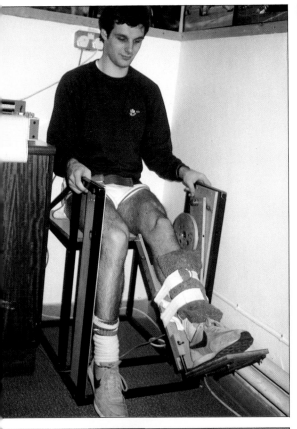

3

4

*Machines and equipment aid a speedy recovery from injury: **1** A machine that measures muscle strength: it is used to chart the progress of an injured muscle during a recovery programme. **2** A leg press machine can help to build up an injured leg muscle. **3** and **4** Two shots of a wobble board, which is used to increase mobility in an injured ankle. The board also trains the injured ankle to remember how to balance: this is known as 'proprioception'. There are other objects, such as bouncers, blocks of wood, etc, that are used in the rehabilitative process, which will be discussed.*

will be needed to regain previous conditioning levels on return to sport. Therefore, a comprehensive programme of stretching, strengthening and cardiovascular fitness must be maintained during the whole recovery process.

Passive and Active Exercise

The goals in rehabilitating an injured sportsman are a little different from those for the ordinary non-sportsperson. Vigorous, intense and controlled exercise permits an early return to sport. Passive exercises are begun immediately followed by active exercises, and a sheet of exercises is given to the patient with special instructions on which can be performed at home. Meanwhile, at the Clinic, a graduated programme of progressive resistance exercises is begun to promote strength, endurance, flexibility, speed and co-ordination. Specific exercises are then practised for the injured part, and fitness maintenance is mandatory throughout the rehabilitation programme – especially cardio-respiratory fitness.

Three of the machines in the Masolet sequence exercise programme, devised by two Norwegian physiotherapists. They are from left to right: the leg press, the arm press, and the abdominal exerciser.

The rehabilitation programme places increasing loads on the injured part, and the athlete should be confident that he has been put in a situation that is more stressful than competition. Before returning to activity, clinical assessment by the therapist or doctor must be made. The patient must have normal joint, muscle and tendon function. Partially-healed injuries are re-injured if subjected to stresses that they are not capable of withstanding. It should be remembered that although normal strength can be restored in the Rehabilitation Programme, *skill* is required for the proper use of this strength, and skill patterns are restored or re-learned only by specific *practice* on the field. This is where the expertise of the coach is sought, and the following guidelines are suggested to him:

1 Thorough warm-up with plenty of stretching, especially of the injured part.

2 General warm-up followed by specific warm-up

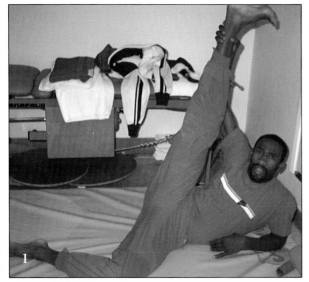

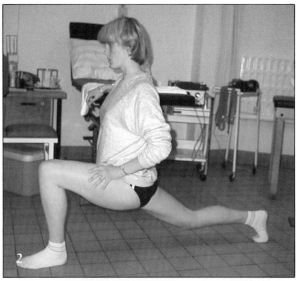

1 Stretches – proper stretching exercises before activity help to warm up the muscles. 2 Lunges – they help to loosen and stretch muscles and to increase flexibility. 3 The Masolet arm pull machine exercises shoulders. 4 Exercise bicycle – spending five minutes on an exercise bike is a good way to loosen the body.

for the sport.

3 Build up skills gradually.

4 No explosive work until later.

5 Do not train through pain.

6 Re-assess after training session.

7 Thorough warm-down.

Good coaching, officiating, equipment and facilities are essential for the prevention of injury.

Weight-Training

Weight-training plays an important role in the rehabilitation of the sportsman after injury, and in the *prevention* of de-conditioning. Fitness maintenance is of prime importance during the whole rehabilitation programme, and must be maintained while the injury is healing. As Roy Steven and Irvin Richard claim in their book *Sports Medicine*, rehabilitation is started while the healing process is still taking place, resulting in an improved quality of tissue formation during healing. A programme of rehabilitation must be started as soon as possible for the injured part, and in the reconditioning programme emphasis must

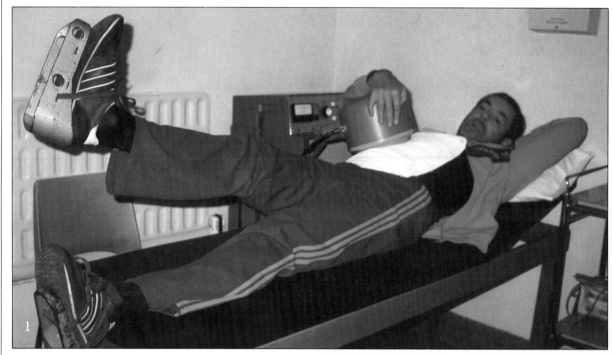

1 *Lifting a 'heavy boot' to strengthen a weak knee.*
2 *Using a length of rubber tubing for resistance.*
3 *Ankle wrestling, which uses the uninjured foot for resistance.*

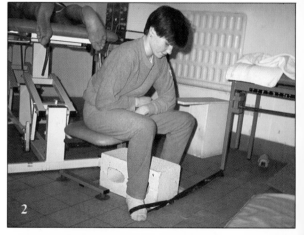

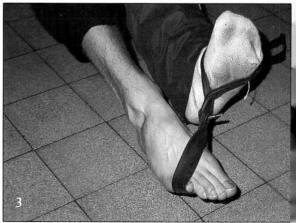

be placed on strength, muscular endurance, cardio-respiratory endurance and flexibility. Un-used muscles can suffer atrophy from disuse and become inflexible, while healing is delayed because of impairment to the circulation system. This is why a balance between rest and exercise is essential during the healing process.

Rehabilitation must deal with the *total* person, not just with the injured part; therefore, fitness maintenance is of prime importance, especially cardio-respiratory fitness. Swimming and station-ary cycling are incorporated into the Rehabili-tation Programme in the early stages, and physical fitness is maintained by weight-training. This allows a safe return to sport in the shortest poss-ible time for the sportsperson.

Therapeutic Exercises

Therapeutic exercises are concerned with main-taining muscular strength, muscular endurance, flexibility, co-ordination and speed of movement. **Muscular strength** is one of the most essential factors in the restoration of function following injury. Muscle size and strength decrease with disuse, and this must be prevented if possible. In the reconditioning programme, both isometric and isotonic muscular contractions are used to advantage (their definitions follow).

Isometric contractions are used initially when pain is present and when movement of the limb is prohibited – ie. when swelling is present, or there are sutures *in situ* or the limb is in a cast. Isometric exercises involve no movement of the joints but develop strength primarily in the *position exercised*. These exercises are started almost immediately to maintain muscle tone and strength. The classic example is the Quadriceps 'Set', or bracing of the thigh muscles and holding the contraction for a number of seconds to gain and maintain strength. Isometric exercises may also be done when the limb is immobilized in a cast to prevent muscle atrophy. Isometric exercises increase strength in the range in which the exercise is performed.

Isotonic exercises are begun when there are no contraindications – ie. sutures out, no cast, no swelling, etc. They are preferable to isometric as they increase function through the complete range of motion, and not just at specific angles.

Most therapeutic exercise programmes employ the overload principle for strengthening muscles in accordance with the De Lorme method of progressive resistance exercises (PRE). This method basically uses ten repetitions for each set, and three sets are usually completed in a session. The sequence set down by De Lorme is that the first set is performed using half the maximum resistance load, the second set uses three-quarters maximum load and the third set uses the full resistance load. This method may be modified according to the type of training programme prescribed for the individual. Sets may be increased to three × twenty-five repetitions with light weights to develop muscular endurance. For strength to be developed the weight is increased and the repetitions are decreased.

High intensity exercise: when performing high intensity exercise, only eight repetitions should be performed. If these cannot be completed, then the load is too heavy. However, twelve to fifteen repetitions can be performed, then the load is too light. High intensity contractions should only be practised two to three times per week, as total recovery from this kind of training requires at least forty-eight hours. During the early stages of

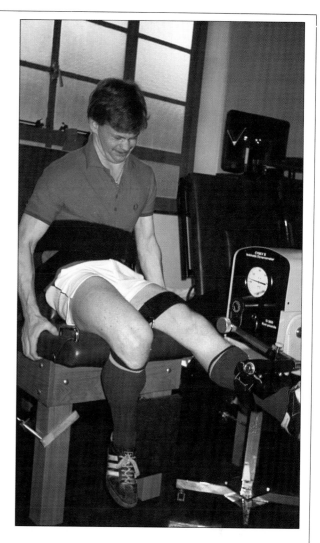

A 'Cybex' machine, which can be set at different speeds for exercising an injured muscle: the patient provides the resistance. This is known as 'Isokinetic' exercise, which is very useful for developing strength, power and endurance.

rehabilitation, the intensity of the work-out is so low that daily work-outs are possible. Later, as the intensity increases, training is reduced to two to three times per week. Weight-training can do many things to the athlete: improve his strength, speed, endurance and explosive power, as well as enhance his general well-being. It is essential, however, that the weight-training is correctly carried out. Certain *fundamental principles* must be followed in the weight-training session:

1 A general warm-up, including stretching.
2 All movements are started from a position of stretch.
3 Movements are performed slowly and smoothly.
4 When the exercise becomes easy – add more weight.

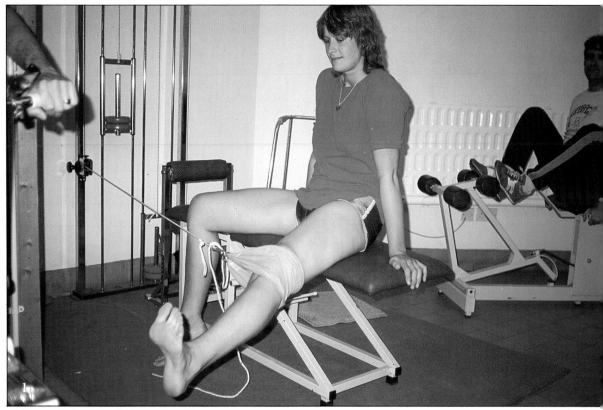

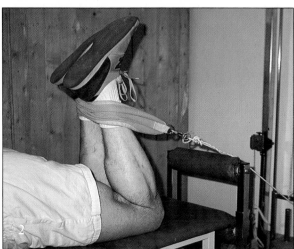

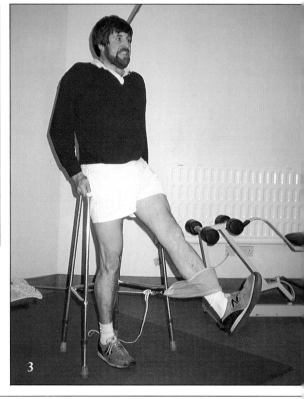

1 *The pulley regime can be used to exercise all four muscle groups of the legs: the quadriceps, hamstrings, abductors and adductors. This exercise reaches the abductors.*

2 *The ham curl exercise performed on a pulley system, for the backs of the calves.*

3 *Exercising the hip through a pulley system.*

5 Exercise the muscles on each side.

6 Work with weights on alternate days.

7 General body conditioning precedes specific exercises for sport.

8 When using weight machines in a circuit-type programme, incorporate the weights regime into the specific warm-up, using light weights and ten to fifteen repetitions only.

Progressive resistance exercises require good form if they are to be valuable. Proper form includes: speed of movement, range of motion, and beginning the movement from a pre-stretched position. The resistance must be moved in a smooth fashion – not jerkily. The range of movement must be as great as possible as muscles must be strengthened throughout their active range.

Stretching and strengthening exercises enhance each other and must be combined to ensure stability around the joints. Stretching must always be part of the strengthening programme, and the muscles must be trained from the 'on stretch' position to a maximal contraction, to full stretch again. Muscles that are trained for strength alone become thicker and shorter, therefore the range of motion at the joint is decreased. The aim of stretching is to increase the range of motion to enable one to reach more extreme body positions, and increase skill and power by permitting the muscles to work over a greater range. Correct form should be constantly stressed in order to maximize the results, and also to prevent injury.

Pre-stretching the muscle by allowing it to be pulled into a position of increased tension prior to contraction, allows the trainee to handle heavier weights and to bring into action more muscle mass during each repetition. The load must be heavy enough to require a maximal contraction.

Injury-Prevention and Safety during Weight-Training

The motto is '*train, don't strain*'.

Warm-up: a good warm-up is not only essential for injury-prevention but allows one to become both physically and mentally prepared for the training session ahead. Maintaining proper *flexibility* is also very important. Flexibility exercises must accompany strength training.

Stretching: proper stretching exercises before activity can help to warm the muscles and increase blood flow. After activity, they help muscles to cool down slowly and can prevent any sudden 'pooling' of the blood.

Correct technique: learn proper technique using light weights before the load is increased. Lift with the legs and protect the back from undue stress. The flat-back position (pelvic tilt) should be assumed in all exercises done – seated or standing – where there is a possibility of the spine getting out of alignment. Therefore, avoid a curvature or swayback during lifting.

Breathing: breath-holding during exercise should be avoided, since it increases pressure within the chest cavity. The increased pressure causes a rapid rise in blood pressure which, in turn, diminishes the cardiac output and slows the venous return. This leads to a rapid decrease in blood pressure. Known as the 'Valsalva Manoeuvre,' this rapid chain of events can cause dizziness, faintness, headache and even blackout.

More rules for weight-training

1 Just remember: no breath-holding, and exhale on effort!

2 Wear trainers when exercising to protect feet from a dropped weight or barbell.

3 Ensure that the collars are tight so that the weights are secure on the bar.

4 Be sure that the support pin is in place when using stacked weight equipment.

5 Record each weight-session to enable you to progress gradually. Records will show any improvement and further motivate you in your effort to regain fitness.

The five principles of weight-training:

1 Keep it gradual – increase resistance slowly.

2 Specificity – make sure the exercise is executed correctly.

3 Control of movement – lift and lower the weight smoothly.

4 Complete the range of motion – work through to full range.

5 Pain-free – if pain results, reduce the weight or stop the exercise.

Time and Goals

Weight-training is of prime importance in the rehabilitation of the injured sportsman, both for fitness maintenance and re-conditioning. Fitness training is started immediately for the rest of the body, except for the injured part. Any injury has to be rehabilitated slowly, as despite all the electrical modalities used, and the various therapeutic techniques, Nature will take its course and this means *time* for the healing process to occur. A sound programme will put this time to good use by setting goals for the injured sportsman, and keeping him busy maintaining fitness for the rest of the body while the injury is healing.

The Importance of First Aid

There are many stages of therapeutic treatment that precede weight-training for the injured part, one of which is the initial first aid. Rehabilitation *starts* with first aid. A successful return to sport can often depend on the judgement of the first contact with the injury, and the application of the appropriate first aid. Previous injury predisposes to recurrence of further injury if proper rehabilitation is not undertaken. Therefore, the athlete may be competing too soon with instability, a lack of muscular co-ordination and muscle weakness. The aim of treatment is to restore full function to the injured muscle and get the sportsman back to his sport as soon as possible.

The Four Types of Therapeutic Exercise

Therapeutic exercises, after injury, are divided into four categories:
1 Passive
2 Assisted
3 Active
4 Resisted

Passive exercise is the movement of a part by another person without any effort by the injured person. This technique is used by physiotherapists to increase or maintain the range of motion in a joint, or to alleviate fear when the patient is apprehensive about moving an injured limb.

Assisted exercises simply mean active movement of a limb with assistance by the other limb (auto-assistance), or with the assistance of another person. The patient is actively doing the exercise, initially with gravity assistance, and then against gravity itself.

Active exercise means exercising by the patient himself without any assistance by another. These exercises are used widely in the restoration of function to the injured part – ie. in isometric exercises to gain and maintain muscle strength, and isotonic exercises to maintain full range of motion about the joints.

Resisted exercises (weight exercises) are those exercises performed against a resistive force and can be isometric or isotonic in nature. In the rehabilitation of an injured sportsman, many different forms of resistance are used which can also be considered as weight-training. Examples of resistance devices are:
1 Working against the manual resistance of the therapist as in P.N.F.
2 Using the other limb as a weight, eg. placing one leg on top of the other and lifting it.
3 Using the body as the resistive force, eg. rope-climbing, press-ups.
4 Using weighted medicine balls, weighted belts, weighted boots, barbells and dumb-bells.
5 Using rubber tubing, springs and pulleys. For training at home, bike tubes are used for resistance: a set routine can be improvised for various muscle groups.
6 Using weight-lifting equipment.
7 Stationary bicycle.
8 Water is also used as a resistive force. Thus, progressive resistance in water can be accomplished by increasing the speed of movement, the number of repetitions, the depth of exercising, or by using devices such as paddles, webbed gloves, flippers on the feet, etc.

Circuit training: when the athlete is nearing full recovery, all muscles can be placed under maximal stress by incorporating CT into the rehabilitation programme.

Sport specific skills: no athlete is rehabilitated until he has developed the ability to perform the movements required by his sport. These exercises should become more complex as the rehabilitation programme progresses.

Isometric, Isotonic and Isokinetic Exercises Explained

Isometric exercises

Isometric exercise does not produce any joint motion, and the muscle contracted does not change in length. The contraction is often performed against a fixed resistance. Strength is gained only at the angle of contraction. To achieve the greatest benefit, the joint should be at an angle that will permit maximal contraction of the muscle, eg, Quadriceps 'setting' with the knee fully extended. Very often muscle stimulation is used to produce an isometric contraction in an inhibited muscle due to pain and swelling after injury.

Isotonic exercises

Isotonic exercises produce joint movement. The contracting muscle shortens and this produces the movement. Isotonic exercises may be performed against the resistance of fixed weights, such as sandbags, boots, springs, pulleys, tubes, Universal Weight machines, etc. Isotonic exercises are used in Progressive Resistance Regimes. They consist of 'concentric' movement when the muscle shortens and the weight is lifted, and 'eccentric' movement, when the muscle lengthens as the weight is lowered. It is the eccentric work that can produce greater strength, but at a cost of greater muscle soreness.

It is often possible to lower a much heavier weight than can be lifted, and this principle is often used in rehabilitation. The lifting of the weight is assisted and it is then lowered unassisted. Isotonic exercises produce improvement by developing tension within the muscle. More tension is developed at a slow, controlled rate of movement. One disadvantage of isotonic exercise, however, is that the weight is determined by the weakest part of the range of motion. Therefore, except for this point, the rest of the muscle range of motion is working sub-maximally. Variable resistance machines are now available to overcome this problem.

The knee flexion extension machine using isotonic weight resistance is the most frequently used rehabilitation device in the United Kingdom. Exercises may be done in many different ways – for example, lifting the weight with both legs and lowering with the affected leg, or lifting and lowering with the affected leg alone.

Isokinetic exercise is an accommodating vari-able resistance in which the speed of motion is set and the resistance accommodates to match the force applied. The speed settings range from 0° per second to 300° per second. It is important to note that strength is usually developed between 60° per second and 120° per second, while power

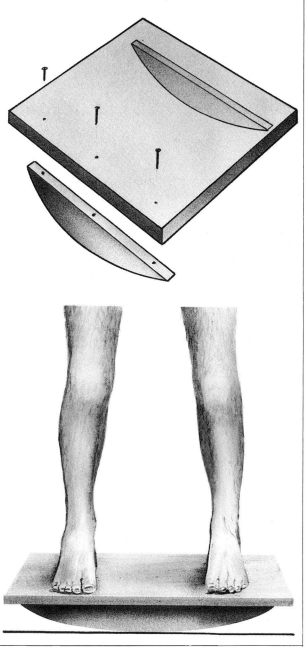

To increase ankle mobility following an injury, a wobble board is quite useful. It is easy to construct: put together a wooden board two feet square, with two pieces of wood cut into a concave shape as shown in the diagram.

is developed at around 180° per second. One advantage of these machines is the visual read-out, which helps to evaluate progress and acts as a powerful psychological stimulus for the athlete. As the resistance is accommodating, the athlete can reduce the force at the point of pain. Isokinetic rehabilitation machines are exceptionally useful in developing strength, power and endurance. It is suggested that the starting speed of exercising should be about 120° per second, progressing up to 180° per second and then to 300° per second.

Another form of accommodation variable resistance is **manual resistive exercises**. The therapist can adjust the speed of movement and resistance to suit the patient's needs at a particular stage of rehabilitation. Manual resistance can exercise patterns of movement that cannot be duplicated on machines.

In summary, there is a wide variety of strength-training equipment available, some of which is very expensive. The important thing is not the kind of equipment one uses, but how it is used.

Balancing Muscle Groups

It is important that the exercise programme gives equal balance to the opposite muscle groups – for instance, when biceps are worked, equal attention must be given to the opposing muscle groups (antagonists), triceps. This principle also applies to the regions of the body. A balanced programme should exercise the upper and lower extremities. Besides beginning a good, balanced programme, specific exercises for sport must be included. Let us take an example from the world of running: for short-distance runners and explosive sports, power is most important; and for longer distance and recreational sports, muscular endurance is most important. A sprinter, for example, will need to develop hamstring strength to the fullest, whereas the long-distance runner achieves hamstring strength while running. Distance runners need to strengthen those muscles at the front of the body – abdominals, quadriceps and Tibialis Anterior (front of leg) muscles to balance the strength gained in the Gastrochnemius, hamstrings and long back muscles through running. Now let us look at the treatment of a specific injury.

Progressive Steps in the Rehabilitation of the Knee after Injury

The muscles around the knee atrophy very quickly after knee injury, especially the quadriceps and hamstring muscle groups; even though the joint may be immobilized and painful, muscle strength and tone must be maintained. This is done by isometric progressive resistance exercises. First, the patient must do quadriceps Sets. These consist of tightening the front of the thigh muscles maximally, paying particular attention to Vastus Medialis (the muscle that locks the knee into full extension) and holding this isometric contraction for five to ten seconds. This exercise must be done for five minutes every waking hour.

Hamstring sets are performed in the same manner by pushing the foot backwards against resistance and maintaining the isometric contraction for five to ten seconds.

Straight leg raises (SLR) are the next progression and are done in various positions in order to strengthen all the muscles around the knee joint. The SLR exercises for the quadriceps are performed in the sitting position, on a mat, with the legs straight in front. The leg is raised up and lowered, and held at various angles during the regime. This is also done in the lying position. Fifteen non-stop SLR with maximum resistance are performed each hour while awake.

SLR for abduction and adduction are done in the side-lying position, and when the patient lies prone and extends the leg backwards, the Gluteal and hamstring muscles are exercised. To make progress, resistance is added first manually, then with weights, and finally the exercises are executed at the pulley machine, where full range of motion can be obtained in the hip joint. Straight Leg Resisted exercises are performed at the pulley as long as knee flexion is contra-indicated, ie. immobilization in a cast, swelling and various other conditions that would be aggravated by knee flexion.

In the meantime, range of motion exercises for the knee joint are initiated, first by passive exercise (controlled by the therapist) progressing to active and manual resistance exercises through the full range of motion. To gain full flexion or extension of the knee joint, the therapist usually

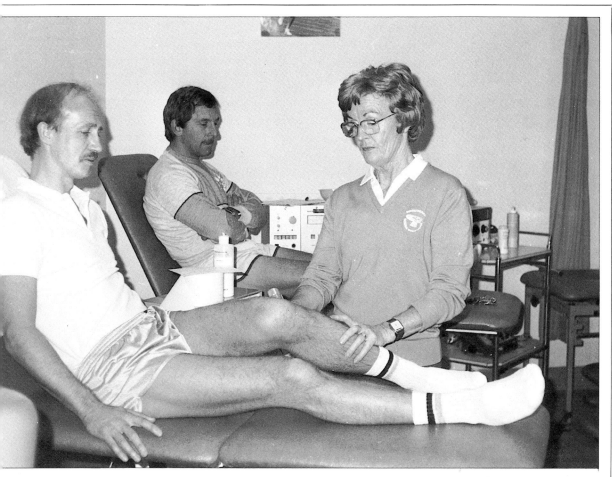

uses the PNF method (Proprioceptive Neuro-muscular Facilitation).

The 'Contract – Relax – Stretch' method is accomplished by the patient executing a maximum isometric contraction of one muscle group, which is immediately followed by a maximum relaxation of the same muscle group: thus a fully relaxed muscle will adapt more easily to stretch. At this stage, the stationary bicycle is incorporated into the programme. First, by pedalling backwards (no resistance) with the saddle fairly high. As range of motion increases, the saddle is lowered until range of motion is full and painfree. Progression is made to normal pedalling, with appropriate resistance, and timed periods are begun on the bicycle. Of primary importance in this process is the achievement of painfree flexion and full extension.

Building Strength

As joint motion and flexibility return, resistance exercises are increased. The therapist applies the resistance, which will vary as the range of motion increases. Spiral movement patterns are executed by the patient against manual resistance, which may be varied at various angles to accommodate the weaker muscle groups. The maximal contraction of the strong muscles facilitates the contraction of the weaker muscles through recruitment. This 'overflow' principle can be used from one muscle group to another, or from one limb to another.

Cross education or bilateral transfer of training is a very important concept in rehabilitating the injured part. This refers to the ability of the nervous system to transfer some of the effects achieved by training one part of the body to the bilaterally opposite part. For example, when a limb on one side of the body is exercised intensively over a period of time, the strength of the corresponding (bilateral) limb on the opposite side of the body also improves. Thus, when a patient has one leg immobilized in a cast, exercising the uninjured leg on the weight machine will gradually improve the strength in the immobilized limb.

Pulley Regime

After a general warm-up and ten minutes on the bike, the routine is begun with a 2½–5 kg weight depending on the muscle strength of the patient. The legs are exercised through hip flexion, extension, abduction and adduction. That way, all four muscle groups are exercised: the quadriceps, hamstrings, abductors (Glu. med and Tensor f.lata) and adductors (gracilis adductors longus, brevis and magnus).

The routine begins with three sets of ten repetitions and progresses to a maximum of three × twenty-five repetitions. As the weight is gradually increased, the repetitions are dropped back to three × fifteen and progress to the maximum again. The weight most used in the straight leg routine weighs 12½kg.

When the patient has full flexion of the knee, hamstring curls are added to the routine. Both legs are exercised together to begin with, then one leg at a time. Care must be taken not to neglect the calf muscles during this time; therefore, a routine of stretching and strengthening exercises is incorporated into the rehabilitation programme. The patient stands on an inclined board or rocker or step; the heels are dropped using body weight to stretch the Achilles tendons and calf muscles; then heel raises are done using the body as the resistive force. This exercise is performed with both feet initially, then unilaterally. As strength increases, each leg is exercised twenty-five times, building up to fifty repetitions. Small weights may be added to the shoulders as strength increases; whereas wobble boards and bouncers are used for the knee and ankle.

When strength permits, the patient moves on to the leg press where much heavier weights are used. Initially, endurance is built up, then the repetitions are decreased and the weights are increased. Pyramids may be used at this time, and eventually a maximum of eight to ten repetitions are done with maximal weight. To determine the

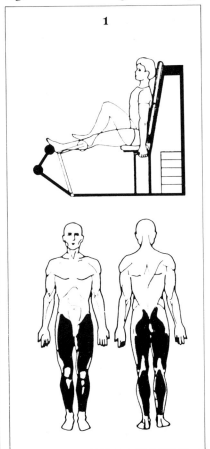

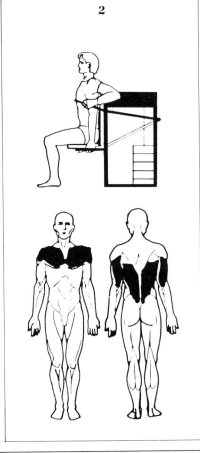

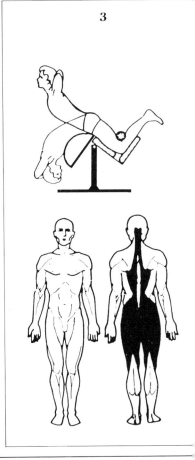

maximum weight that can be lifted in a set, choose the weight that can be lifted – more than eight but less than twelve times – (this equals ten repetitions maximum). Three sets of ten repetitions are then performed at 50 per cent, 75 per cent and 100 per cent of the ten repetition maximum, which is determined once weekly and adjusted accordingly.

As strength is developed, more emphasis is placed on speed, power and endurance, circuit-training techniques and flexibility exercises. At the end, specific skill patterns are prescribed – progressing to complex skills. Before a return to sport can be planned, the injured limb should equal the uninjured in muscle strength, power and endurance. There must be balance between antagonistic muscle groups. Flexibility around the joint must be equal as well as proprioception and functional use of the limb.

Summary

Weight-training is an integral part of the rehabilitation process, and patients are encouraged to continue this form of exercise after they have been discharged as fit for sport. Circuit training on weight machines gives a vigorous all-round work-out in a short time, and leads to progressive development of muscular and cardio-respiratory endurance. It is an alternative form of training and is an excellent method for gaining and maintaining fitness after injury.

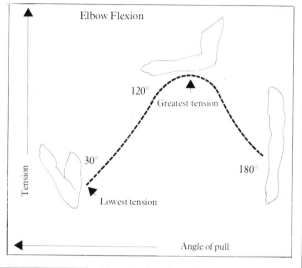

Above: during elbow flexion, the tension developed when lifting a constant load varies according to the joint angle: the greatest tension (strength) of the biceps muscle is obtained at a joint angle of about 120°, whereas the least tension is obtained at 30°.

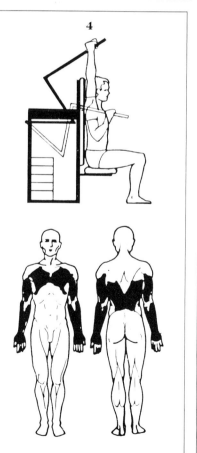

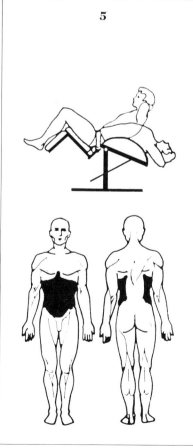

Left: the five machines used in the Masolet Sequence Exercise Programme, together with the main muscle groups involved, are: 1 Leg press (for leg and hip joint muscles). 2 Arm press (for arm and chest muscles). 3 Back extension (for back and buttock muscles). 4 Arm pull (for arm and shoulder muscles). 5 Abdominal exerciser (for abdominal muscles only). The five machines are set up in a circuit, allowing the trainer 20 seconds on each machine with a 10 seconds' rest in between. This works specific muscle groups without overlap and thus avoids muscle fatigue. The number of circuits performed is decided by the coach, depending on the fitness level of the individual.

PROFILE:
PAUL STIMPSON

WEIGHT-TRAINING AFTER INJURY

Paul Stimpson, 26, has been captain of the English basketball team for the last three years. He had done some light weight-training as a member of the Crystal Palace Junior Men's Team in London and while at college, but he did not think about taking it up seriously until 1983 – on November 25th of that year, he slipped on a basketball court in Manchester, fracturing and dislocating his left ankle.

After consulting a specialist, it was obvious that he needed an operation: the following month two small screws were put into his left ankle, as well as a 10cm/4in pin to immobilize it until it healed. As a result, Paul was laid up in plaster for six weeks, followed by another operation to remove the pin. (The two screws are still in his ankle, and will have to be removed eventually in order to prevent Paul developing osteo-arthritis.)

The X-rays had shown that Paul had the ankles of a forty-year-old man; all that basketball playing had created spurs and callouses on his ankle bones that could be spotted on the X-ray. Two weeks after his second operation, Paul was given basic exercises at the physiotherapy department of the Westminster Hospital in London to get his leg moving again. He graduated from crutches to a walking stick, and then found himself under the supervision of Rose Macdonald, head physiotherapist at Crystal Palace Sports Centre. After reading his case notes and making sure that he could move his ankle, she gave him a programme of daily massage and ultrasound. Paul worked his ankle against manual resistance until he could manage a full range of movement. He then worked out on a pulley system that strapped around his ankle, so that every time he lifted his leg his ankle was being worked. He used the leg press machine and did hours of cycling to build up the injured ankle's strength. Rose continued the massage and ultrasound and when Paul was

ready, she moved him on to circuit training on the Masolet equipment. He started with three circuits of ten pounds on each machine, and only progressed to more weight and repetitions when Rose told him he was ready.

His own doctor had told him not to even *think* of playing for six months, but the specialist was more open-minded, saying it depended on how well his bones mended. Paul, however, was determined. By mid-January he was out of plaster; he knew his first match was on March 4th, and that gave him six weeks to get fit.

Every week, Rose tested the strength of his left leg, to see how it compared with that of his right one. He did his weight-training faithfully three or four days a week (with a day's rest in between each session) and added swimming three times a week to build up his leg. His pool work consisted of running in water, using the water as resistance, and then adding flippers while swimming to increase endurance in the injured ankle.

In early March, Rose and the specialist gave him the go-ahead and he made the first match on March 4th with his ankle taped to avoid excessive movement. He continued to play a few games until April (meanwhile continuing the swimming and weights work), and then accompanied the Great Britain team to Boston, Massachusetts, for three weeks of training and selection for the Olympic team. Paul was selected, and Great Britain were placed fifth in the qualifying rounds in Paris. Unfortunately, as only the top three European teams were allowed to go to Los Angeles, Paul just missed out on competing in the 1984 Olympics Games.

He now feels that the muscle of his left ankle is as strong as before, although the ligaments and tendons around it are still building up to their former strength. He is confident that his ankle will be as strong as before the accident within a

Weight-training helped Paul return to the English basketball team only six weeks after a fractured ankle.

year – one good sign is that it does not bother him when he is playing. Of his weight-training work, Paul says that it was "invaluable", but he warns other injured sportsmen to ensure that they are supervized when undertaking remedial exercise – "Otherwise", he says, "there's a danger of going nuts and overdoing it, and damaging yourself further, or not doing enough and causing the healing process to take longer than it should". A physiotherapist will tell you how much to do and when to increase the repetitions and weight, by careful observation and regular mobility checks on the injured part. (Rose gave Paul a programme

of little exercises to do as well, and put him on a wobble board to increase muscular 'proprioception' – the feeling of 'balance' experienced by the receptors within the joints.)

Paul will one day undertake that third operation to have those two small screws removed – that is, when he can find two weeks to spare, which is the length of time he will be laid up. His last words on weight-training were: "I thought I had trained hard before – but I never trained as hard as that for basketball!" Rose confirms this: "An injured athlete must be placed in situations that are more stressful than any competition he might take part in – *that* is when you know he is really fit and ready to return to his sport".

CHAPTER NINE
NUTRITION FOR WEIGHT-TRAINING

Most dedicated weight-trainers find that they can perform better if they eat a really healthy diet which provides optimum nutrients and the right number of calories for weight control and energy. Regular training is not the only way to peak performance – if you make special demands on your body and fail to eat healthy food you may never reach your full potential. Many modern weight-trainers rate nutrition and diet as highly as their training schedules. By analysing your diet and identifying its deficiencies and strengths you can adapt it to a healthier regime.

It is just as important for the aspiring weight-trainer to think about the food that he or she is eating as it is to concentrate on a correct and effective programme of exercise. In fact, diet may be *more* important – after all, the food that you eat is providing the fuel with which you train.

There has been a great deal of confusion in recent years as to what constitutes a healthy diet; the public have been bombarded with information, not only from scientists and the government, but from self-interest groups like the meat-and-dairy farmers' lobby, the food industry and the slimming industry. In 1979, the National Advisory Committee on Nutrition Education (NACNE) was set up by the government to establish clear guidelines on a healthy diet. The results of their research confirmed what many medical authorities had been saying for years – that most British people (and, indeed, the peoples of all Western societies) ate too much fat, sugar and salt, and not enough wholefoods, fresh vegetables and fruit. Their guidelines on the consumption of the offending items are as follows:
1 Reduce fat by a quarter (from 40 to 30 per cent of all calories consumed).
2 Cut sugar by half (from 20 to 10 per cent of total calories).
3 Cut salt by half (from 10 grams to 5 grams a day).

They also advised that fibre be increased by half as much again (from 20 to 30 grams a day).

There is a more sinister fact that surfaced in NACNE's nutritional research, and that is the connection between our fatal illnesses (cancer and heart disease, for instance) and diet. Although lung cancer, which is linked to cigarette smoking, is our leading cancer-killer, it is quickly followed by cancer of the large bowel, which is closely linked to the typical Western lifestyle and diet. In our society, the pendulum has swung away from starvation and diseases resulting from nutritional deficiency, and towards diseases resulting from eating too much of the wrong kinds of food.

Leading nutritionists all agree that everyone should look at their diet, and none more so than the athlete and weight-trainer. In the build-up to the 1984 Olympic Games, world-class athletes in Britain began to 'eat to win'. One such internationally-known athlete was Brian Hooper, pole vaulter, who, at the age of 28, discovered wholefoods and subsequently went on to set five British pole vault records through his improved performance. He was already working from a strong foundation with a rigorous training programme; he merely proceeded to cut out sugar, reduce salt, and concentrate on unrefined carbohydrates and plenty of vegetables and fruit. He also took vitamin and mineral supplements. The change in his diet produced many benefits for Brian; apart from a general improvement in his athletic prowess, he discovered that he recovered more quickly from training sessions and succumbed to far fewer illnesses and injuries. He also noticed that he could sustain top-rate performances over longer periods of time. Brian's views on nutrition are no longer unique. Any athlete or sportsperson who is serious about performing to maximum capacity has put nutrition alongside training in importance. Weight-trainers, especially, are making great physical demands on their bodies: they cannot hope to feed their bodies only protein for muscle-building and sugary snacks for quick energy, and obtain high levels of performance (the reason for this will be discussed under 'Carbohydrates').

The Nutrients in Our Food

First, let us look at the nutrients that food provides in general. These are: proteins, carbohydrates, fats, vitamins, minerals and water. These six basic nutrients each have a special role to play, but they also interact with each other. In our digestive tracks, enzymes and acids interact with these nutrients to transform proteins into amino acids, carbohydrates to sugars, and fats into fatty acids and glycerol.

These new forms are then absorbed into the bloodstream: fats and fat-soluble vitamins proceed directly to the cells, while other nutrients are sent to the liver to be worked on first by special enzymes. The process by which digested nutrients are turned into building blocks and energy for the body is called *metabolism*. And this is where vitamins and minerals play a part: in order for enzymes to do their work properly, certain vitamins and minerals must be present, and they will be discussed in turn.

Protein

A protein is a chain of amino acids (composed of carbon, hydrogen, oxygen and nitrogen); there are 23 in all, and only 14 of them can be made in the body. The remaining nine amino acids must be obtained from the food we eat. 'Complete protein' is found in milk, eggs, fish, meat and poultry, and 'incomplete protein' (ie, the missing nine) can be found in rice, beans, lentils and wheat germ. If you combine certain foods in the 'incomplete' section – rice with beans, for instance – you are supplied with the missing nine amino acids. Protein forms the building blocks of cells, and allows growth and repair to take place. Any extra is converted into glucose for energy.

The body can only assimilate a small amount of protein at a time, so if you are eating protein to build up muscle, take it in five to six small meals a day instead of two small meals and one big one. You may wish to supplement your daily intake with protein drinks that can be mixed with milk if you are interested in training for weight gain, but get advice on how often they should be taken: you do not want to put on more weight than you can train into muscle.

Many weight-trainers who have based their diets on red meat and eggs (both good sources of protein) became alarmed when the dangers of cholesterol hit the headlines. Although the link between the amount of cholesterol you eat and the amount of cholesterol in your *bloodstream* is unclear, medical evidence shows that a high cholesterol diet *usually* causes high blood cholesterol. The body can still obtain cholesterol from foods that are high in saturated fats (butter, beef, pork, cakes and chocolate), so these foods need to be decreased as well as the cholesterol-containing ones (egg yolk, dairy produce and animal fat). Cholesterol is a natural product of the body (it is synthesized in the liver to make bile acids), but as we only need such a small amount of it, it is wise to cut back as much as possible in view of its connection with heart disease.

And what about vegetarian weight-trainers? Can they actually obtain sufficient protein from whole-grains and other foods? The answer is 'yes', as long as they drink milk and eat cheese (to top up vitamin B12), and balance their foods carefully. Vegans, of course, can avoid the problems of cholesterol and saturated fats that accompany meat and animal products altogether. Unless he is body-building or competing in a sport, that requires muscle power like the shot put, the average weight-trainer can afford to have smaller meat portions (alongside larger portions of starches and vegetables), and even switch over to lean white meat. Vegetarians sometimes do not get enough iron or zinc, but if this is watched and compensated for, there are no serious deficiencies that would impede a vegetarian weight-trainer from attaining his or her maximum potential.

Carbohydrates

Carbohydrates are composed of three main groups: the starches, sugars and celluloses. The starches, known as complex carbohydrates, are turned into glucose in the body. This glucose provides energy for the brain, the nervous system and the muscles, and is commonly known as 'blood sugar'. Some glucose is converted into glycogen for storage, but excessive amounts are stored as fat. They can be found in whole-grain cereals and flours, brown rice, potatoes, beans, pulses, sweetcorn, bananas, etc (other vegetables contain starch but in smaller amounts). As a group, the starches are better for us than the simple carbohydrates, or sugars, because they break down into glucose more slowly, which means they provide more energy over a longer period of time. They also do not bring with them the problems associated with sugar: obesity, tooth decay, gum disease, and heart and liver disease. The complex carbohydrates are naturally high in fibre, apart from the highly refined carbohydrates like white bread, which provide very little. Whole-wheat bread (with the wheat germ and bran intact), provides eight times more fibre than white bread. Adding a few tablespoonfuls of wheat bran to your food every day will give you enough fibre to meet your needs. Apart from providing the roughage that our intestines need to move food through the digestive track to the bowel for efficient elimination, fibre is also important if you want to lose weight. One test conducted in America in the early 1980s showed that men on a high-fibre diet of 2,500 calories a day absorbed nearly five per cent fewer calories than they did on a low-fibre diet of 2,500 calories. Fibre also reduces the risk of developing intestinal or rectal cancer. The third group of carbohydrates, the celluloses, are pure fibre, being the peelings of fruits and vegetables that we cannot digest; they pass along our digestive track taking waste matter with them.

Two other types of starch are dextrin and glycogen. Dextrin is formed from starch when grains sprout; it is broken down to glucose in the digestive track. Glycogen is a form of starch stored in animal bodies; liver is a particularly rich source. Glycogen is also broken down into glucose, so even a complete meat-eater like an Eskimo would be consuming 15 per cent's worth of indirect sugar.

The simple carbohydrates, like sugar, corn syrup or honey, serve us merely as a quick source of energy. Because sugar is turned into glucose so rapidly, it provides a sudden energy jolt. The rapid increase in blood sugar, however, causes the pancreas to produce more insulin quickly. This triggers an immediate drop in the level of blood sugar – leaving you drained and craving more sweets. Sugar occurs naturally in fruits and vegetables, so there is no need to supplement this natural fructose with refined sugar and its products. You will thus be protecting your blood sugar level as well as avoiding tooth decay, gum disease, and lessening your chances of suffering from obesity, heart and liver disease. So, apart from refined sugar, stay away from sugar syrups, jams, cakes, biscuits, sweets and all processed foods that are made from refined sugar.

Beware a low-carbohydrate diet

Many weight-trainers think that they can or should eat mostly protein in order to build up muscle tissue. However, there is one thing that they have overlooked: if protein is to build up muscle, where does the energy come from to train on? Without adequate carbohydrate to provide the necessary glucose, the body will simply break down muscle tissue to supply the energy! Without glucose from carbohydrates the brain cannot function properly, leaving you irritable and irrational. Without mental control you may binge on food that is completely unsuitable for you – all because your brain is starved of this vital sugar. If you want to lose weight while weight-training, do *not* cut out carbohydrate, but reduce your calories (especially from fats) slowly over a period of time and increase your training to speed up your metabolism.

Fats

Fats are the most concentrated form of energy, and the *second* most important source of energy for us. Fat contains nine calories per gram, which is twice as many as a gram of protein or carbohydrate. Thus, the easiest way of reducing calories in our diet, should we wish to, is by reducing our fat intake. Apart from energy, fats supply essential fatty acids, as well as lubricating, insulating and protecting our internal organs. There are two kinds of fats: saturated and unsaturated.

Saturated fats are found primarily in animal fats, whole milk, butter, cream, egg yolks, cheese, coconut and palm oils, and many processed foods where fat is often hidden from sight. They may be solid at room temperature and are thought to be harmful, contributing to heart disease and blood problems. Cholesterol, which is associated with saturated fats, clogs up arterial walls, especially in the heart. Your body needs *some* cholesterol, however, and the liver actually synthesizes it. Sedentary people have higher cholesterol levels than people who are active, and weight-trainers will find that their vigorous exercise will help protect their hearts. Some foods offer protection from cholesterol: eggs, although containing cholesterol in the yolk, also have a substance called lechithin in the white, which helps to control cholesterol levels; and nuts have a similar substance called linoleic acid.

Unsaturated fats, which are liquid at room temperature, are found in fish, nut and vegetable oils. The best vegetable oils to use are these: safflower oil (74 per cent polyunsaturated), sunflower oil (64 per cent), corn oil (58 per cent) and soybean oil (57 per cent). As fat tends to accumulate in our bodies (because just a little of it gives us so much energy), try to cut down on your fat intake by eating only low-fat cheeses (like cottage cheese, fromage frais, ricotta and quark), low-fat yoghurt, skimmed milk and lean white meat (chicken and fish). Avoid butter and cream; use lemon juice instead of salad oil; remove the skin and fat from meat and poultry; and buy tuna and sardines canned in brine, not oil. Also, stay away from mayonnaise and fatty, creamy sauces. These measures will help minimize the risk of heart disease and intestinal and breast cancers.

Vitamins

Vitamins are organic substances which the body requires in very small amounts for all the building up and breaking down processes that take place within it. They act as catalysts for biochemical reactions. They help protect us against infection, pollution and stress, and they help improve our general appearance (hair, skin, nails, eyes and teeth). If we lived in a pollution-free world, and ate organically-grown, unadulterated food, we could be sure of getting all the vitamins (and minerals) that we need from our food. As it is, many vegetables and fruits are harvested before they are ripe, transported long distances and stored before being sold. All this results in vitamin loss.

Some vitamins (vitamin C and the B-group) are water-soluble, which means that their vitamin content can be lost in the cooking process. These vitamins have to be topped up daily. However, vitamins A, D, E and K are fat-soluble, which means that they can be stored in the body, and are therefore less at risk. But be very careful when supplementing with fat-soluble vitamins, as high doses can have toxic effects. Whereas vitamin D can actually be made in the body, the rest must be obtained from the food we eat.

There are twelve important vitamins for us (several in the B-group), which will now be listed, along with the foods they are found in and the Recommended Daily Amount (RDA) of each where known. (Amounts quoted are from the Department of Health and Social Security, in their 1979 *Manual of Nutrition*.)

Vitamin A promotes smooth skin and good eyesight, and is absolutely essential for normal growth and development. A deficiency will result in poor vision, fatigue and lowered resistance to infection. It can be found in dark green leafy vegetables, deep orange vegetables, milk, egg yolks, fish liver oils, and in some fruits and meats. **RDA:** 750 μg, for both men and women.

Vitamin B-group: there are several vitamins in this group: B1(thiamine), B2(riboflavin), B6(pyridoxine), B12, niacin, pantothenic acid, and biotin. (Choline and inositol are often listed with the B-complex, but they are not strictly vitamins. They both help in the transport of fat from the liver, and choline can be made in the body.)

Vitamin B1 (thiamine) is particularly important in the oxidation of glucose to provide energy, for good muscle tone, stamina and a healthy nervous system. A deficiency would cause the disease beriberi, but this is not likely to happen in the West, where diets are generally adequate. Weight-trainers should increase their dose of this vitamin through the foods they eat, because of its benefits for endurance while training. It is found in yeast, whole-grains, legumes (peas, beans), liver, nuts and seeds. **RDA:** 1.3mg for men, 1.0mg for women.

Vitamin B2 (riboflavin) acts like thiamine to aid the production of glucose, and affects many metabolic processes. It is also responsible for healthy skin, hair and nails. It is found in milk, brewer's yeast, leafy green vegetables, beans, liver, fish and eggs. **RDA:** 1.6mg for men, 1.3mg for women.

Vitamin B6 (pyridoxine) is important in the metabolism of amino acids and the synthesis of haemoglobin, as well as for growth and the formation of skin collagen. It is found in whole-grains, beans, some vegetables, meat, liver, fish, brown rice and bananas. Women suffering from fluid retention can benefit from this vitamin.

Vitamin B12 is paired with another B-vitamin, folate, as they both work to prevent a condition called pernicious anaemia (improperly-formed red blood cells). It is used in the synthesis of all new cells. It is found in meat, fish and milk products (not butter), whereas folate is found in green vegetables, peas, beans and liver. A very small amount of each is needed, and a deficiency is rare, so no RDA is given.

Niacin is needed for enzymes that are involved in many metabolic processes, particularly in the production of glucose. A deficiency results in pellagra, but this is a disease not likely to be seen in industrialized countries. It is found in brewer's yeast, liver, soybeans, green vegetables, peanuts, whole-grain bread, meat, poultry, fish and milk. **RDA:** 18mg for men, 15mg for women.

Pantothenic acid forms a part of an enzyme which is involved in the synthesis and oxidation of fats. It is found in eggs and liver, and as it is difficult to have a deficiency of it no RDA is given here.

Biotin is cited as a contributory factor in certain types of dermatitis, so therefore it is important for the skin. It is found in liver, brewer's yeast, vegetables, nuts and beans. Again, a deficiency is rare.

Vitamin C is essential for good skin, teeth and gums, for fighting stress and for helping to build all the connective tissue within the body. A deficiency results in the disease scurvy, but this is rare nowadays. Although vitamin C, or ascorbic acid, seems to disappear from the body's tissues when it is fighting infection, there is no scientific proof that large doses will ward off infection (like colds and flu). It is found in fresh fruit and vegetables, especially citrus fruits, blackcurrants, peppers, tomatoes and potatoes. **RDA:** 30mg, for men and women.

Vitamin D is essential for healthy bones and teeth, and is needed for the absorption of calcium and phosphorus. A deficiency leads to rickets – a softening and malformation of the bones in young children. Vitamin D can be made in the body by the action of the sun on the skin, but it is also found in milk, dairy products, egg yolks, tuna and fish liver oils. No RDA is given, as most people get an adequate supply from just being out in the sun – but children and adolescents in winter, and housebound adults, are recommended to take 10μg daily.

Vitamin E is necessary for strong muscles and good circulation, and has an influence on the amount of oxygen used by the muscles. (*Weight-trainers take note:* if the body is well supplied with vitamin E, less oxygen is needed by the muscles for oxidation – therefore, using oxygen more efficiently.) Not much is known about how this vitamin works in our bodies, and claims that it retards the ageing process have yet to be scientifically proved. It is found in vegetable oils, nuts, whole-grain cereals, some vegetables (especially avocado) and wild blackberries.

Vitamin K is necessary for normal liver function and in the clotting of blood. It is found in green vegetables, fruits and yoghurt.

Minerals

Minerals are inorganic substances that are needed by the body to regulate certain metabolic processes and to help build up tissues such as bones and teeth. We need 14 different minerals for good health, in amounts varying from just a trace (hence, the term 'trace' elements) up to large amounts. They enter vegetables and other foods through the soil, and if the soil is deficient in some minerals in certain areas, deficiencies can occur. For example, a chromium deficiency in the soil has been linked to heart-related diseases. Where selenium is found, however, people seem to lead longer, healthier lives, without the incidence of cancer and heart disease. Unfortunately, selenium is not distributed very evenly around the world! Minerals also control the balance, amount and composition of liquids inside and outside of cells. Foods rich in minerals are fresh green vegetables, soy-beans, raw wheat germ, yeast, almonds, corn, apples, spinach, parsley and watercress. Some essential minerals are listed below.

Calcium maintains good bones and teeth, and is essential for blood clotting and as an element in tissue and plasma. It also regulates muscle tone and normal nerve behaviour. It is found in milk, yoghurt, sardines and fortified bread. **RDA:** 500mg, for men and women.

Chlorine is actually a *gas*, but combined with

another element it becomes a chloride. Chloride ions join with hydrogen to make up hydrochloric acid, which is secreted into the stomach to aid digestion. Most diets contain enough of this mineral without any supplementation.

Copper is necessary for proper blood cell production and helps in the storage of iron for haemoglobin formation. It is found in green vegetables.

Iodine is involved in the secretion of thyroxine by the thyroid gland (the gland that regulates metabolism and energy). It also affects hormone production, and growth. It is found in common salt and kelp.

Iron is necessary for the production of haemoglobin. Iron combines with oxygen and is carried through the blood system. It is found in liver, lean meat, eggs, bread, and leafy green vegetables. **RDA:** 10mg for men, and 12mg for women. **Note**: menstruating women may need more.

Potassium helps to keep the skin healthy, and is also necessary for normal growth. Potassium stimulates nerve impulses for muscle contraction. It is found in milk, citrus fruit, bananas, green peppers, green vegetables, apricots, avocados, dried fruits, tomatoes and muscle meats. An ordinary balanced diet contains enough of this mineral.

Sodium is needed for metabolic processes and is essential for muscle and nerve activity. It is found in meat juices, as well as the tissue fluids of plants and animals. Sodium joins with chlorine to form sodium chloride, or salt. All body fluids contain salt. We generally take in enough sodium and sodium chloride, although salt levels should be watched in hot weather or climates, and after several hours of strenuous exertion.

Chromium is essential in the activation of insulin and the extraction of glucose from the bloodstream by the cells. It may be helpful in the treatment of diabetes. A deficiency is not likely to arise in most people.

Cobalt is an essential nutrient. The cobalt atom is at the centre of the B12 vitamin. It has some effect in controlling anaemias, but the minute dosage must be carefully administered. It is found in buckwheat, figs, and many green vegetables.

Fluorine is found in teeth and bones and other tissues in the body. It has been shown that the correct amount of fluorine (or fluoride, as the compound is known) in drinking water can help protect growing teeth from decay by forming stronger enamel. It is also found in fish and tea. No addition to the diet is necessary if drinking water is fluoridated.

Magnesium plays a similar role to calcium in that it forms part of the mineral of the bones. It is an *essential* mineral for life, because it is an important part of many enzyme systems involved in the metabolic processes. As it is a part of chlorophyll, the green colouring matter in plants, it is found in green, leafy vegetables.

Manganese is also an essential trace element for Man. It is very important to the working of enzymes, and may also be linked to the treatment of diabetes. It is found in cereals, legumes, green vegetables and tea. We are unlikely to suffer a deficiency.

Zinc is vital for the metabolism of vitamin A, and is a very important mineral that forms part of many enzyme systems in the body. It repairs tissue, promotes growth, makes skin more supple and less prone to stretch marks, helps remove carbon dioxide and aids the liver in detoxifying alcohol. It appears to be useful in controlling diabetes and in promoting wound healing. Zinc is helpful for a sprained muscle and it is needed particularly by pregnant women, and those women who are on the contraceptive pill or who crash-diet regularly. A low zinc level has been linked to anorexia nervosa. A deficiency can lead to depression and mood swings. It is found in seafood, nuts, whole-grain bread, meat and green vegetables.

Other trace minerals

Aluminium, arsenic, tin, silver, nickel and silicon are found in the body in small amounts, but none seem to be involved in essential metabolic processes. They usually enter the body through cooking pots, preserving cans, etc. It is difficult to ascertain what they do, but the small amounts present are usually neither toxic nor harmful.

Natural or supplement?

Weight-trainers have a quandary: whether to try and get all the vitamins and minerals they need from the food they eat, or to take vitamin and mineral supplements as well. Recent scientific tests have shown that vitamins and minerals work best when they are obtained directly from food but, as we have mentioned earlier, it is not always possible to be completely sure about the quality of food we are eating. Frozen and canned food have lost about half their vitamin content by the time they reach you – canned food can be deficient by 75 per cent! So it is not a bad idea to supplement, especially with water-soluble vitamins, and if you do so, ensure that you take 100 per cent of the recommended daily dose, as they are more effective that way. Take them with meals as they will be more efficiently absorbed into the system. However, do not take more than the RDA, especially in the case of fat-soluble vitamins which may even be harmful in large quantities.

Water

Now is the time to mention a very important fluid, which weight-trainers should drink as much as possible. We need water for almost every bodily function: digestion, regulation of body temperature, transportation of nutrients and removal of waste products. We need to drink at least six to eight glasses of water a day, and that is apart from juice, coffee, tea, and the water found in other drinks – not surprising, if you stop to consider that our bodies are literally 97 per cent water! The problem is that the water we obtain from our taps contains up to 1,500 pollutants, including agricultural and industrial wastes, and chemicals added to destroy bacteria and airborne toxins. Some of these chemicals are known to be carcinogens (cancer-causing). So what do we do? We have two choices: either filter our tap water (filter systems can be bought inexpensively from health food shops), or buy distilled or sparkling pure mineral water. Filtered water reduces toxic copper ions and is one-twentieth of the cost of buying water. It does not have the same high mineral content of bought water, however, and filters need changing after 100 litres of water have passed through them (you can buy spare cartridges). Distilled water lacks minerals as well, although you can get around this by eating mineral-rich foods and taking mineral supplements. Your best bet is sparkling mineral water – the French ones are best, as they are examined carefully and graded by the French government, although there are now many new English and Italian ones that could compete. Drink water between meals, as then it will not dilute the digestive juices. And do not forget that another source of pure water is fresh fruit and vegetables – another good reason for eating them!

Food Additives

This is something a weight-trainer must think about when choosing the food that he or she will eat. Weight-training is strenuous enough without giving your body more of a job to do clearing away pollutants. There are thousands of additives put into our food: over 3,000 are permitted in Great Britain alone. Preservatives, emulsifiers, flavourings, colourings, stabilizers and sweeteners are added to supposedly improve the appearance and flavour of food and to extend its shelf life. Hundreds of these chemicals have not been tested sufficiently for us to know with any certainty that they are *really* safe, nor do we know how these chemicals interact with others once they enter the body. Studies in the United States have shown that quite a few substances can react with – and alter – the composition of the DNA molecules. These, as we know, make up the genetic blueprints for all living species. Apart from being mutagents (possessing the ability to mutate cells), several chemicals have been proven in tests on mice to be carcinogens. The food industry argues that a small dose of a cancer-causing substance causes little or no risk – but cancer experts maintain that there are *no* safe doses of carcinogens. Some believe that there may be a threshold for carcinogen exposure, and that even small doses may build up in the body over a period of time. Therefore, even a very weak dose could push the body's total carcinogen burden over the threshold and into cancer. Among the chemicals that appear to promote or be linked with cancer are saccharin, sodium nitrate and nitrite, or E250 and E251, (found in processed meats, sausages and cheeses), BHT, E321 (a petroleum additive) and some red dyes (as opposed to the innocent red colouring, cochineal). Learn to read labels carefully, and avoid products that contain such questionnable additives as nitrates, saccharin, some artificial colourings and petroleum additives such as BHA (E320) and BHT. We are exposed to carcinogens every day from air and water pollution, X-rays and the ultra-violet rays of the sun. Why should we add to that by taking any chances with the food we eat?

Food Allergies

Which leads us to the topic of food allergies, some of which are *caused* by additives. The yellow dye tartrazine (E102), for example, causes allergic reactions in some people, and also impedes the absorption of essential vitamins and minerals. Some people have a violent reaction to mono-sodium glutamate, in the form of migraine-type headaches and stomach ache. Many people have allergies to various foods, and wheat products (especially the gluten in wheat) and dairy products (milk and cheese in particular) are the main culprits. Symptoms of allergy may include: a craving for sweet foods, insatiable appetite, nervousness, mood swings, extreme fatigue, unexplained irritability, sinus trouble and catarrh, migraines, rashes, eczema and hyper-activity in young children.

If you suspect a certain food is giving you problems, leave it out for a week, and stick to a healthy wholefoods diet. After a week, re-introduce the suspect food, and note down any effects. If you still think there may be an allergy lurking, ask your doctor to refer you to an allergy clinic for further tests.

Tips for a Healthy Diet

You have now been given an insight into what constitutes a healthy diet and what does not. To summarize important points, here is a list of tips to keep in mind for a healthy diet:

1 Reduce your salt intake – salt causes fluid retention, and sodium from salt increases the risk of developing high blood pressure. Try herbs and spices for flavouring instead.

2 Watch your sugar content – despite advertisements claiming that athletes need (refined) sugar for energy, the truth is that you get better energy from carbohydrates, and in a more nutritious form. Refined sugar can be disguised as fructose, glucose, dextrose, maltose, and corn syrup in the foods that you buy, so watch out for these on the labels. Refined white sugar is the leading cause of tooth decay and diabetes; brown sugar, honey and molasses, although containing some minerals, are just as bad for you. Cut down your sugar intake gradually, but avoid artificial sweeteners which are potentially harmful. Better still, use pure, organic honey (available from health food shops), which contains useful minerals like iron, calcium and potassium, as well as all nine essential amino acids. Also, use dried fruit for sweeteners, and look for fruit canned in its own juices rather than in sugar syrup.

3 Cut down on fats – use vegetable margarines instead of butter; choose skimmed milk rather than whole milk, and soft, low-fat cheeses like cottage cheese and ricotta. A pound of fat is 3,500 calories! Grill meat rather than frying it. If you are weight-training to lose weight, omit butter and cream from your diet; stick to lean, white meat with the skin removed; avoid salad dressings and anything canned in oil, dried fruit, avocado, grapes and bananas. Stick to low-calorie fruits like melon, strawberries, and other berries. Once you have reached your ideal weight, work out a sensible eating plan and *stick* to it.

4 No soft fizzy drinks – mineral or distilled water is best for carrying away the waste products created by weight-training, and contains no extra calories.

5 Reduce your alcohol and caffeine intake – both these substances are pollutants, and will slow down your liver and kidneys as these organs work to expel them. Caffeine causes changes in cells, and too much of it can speed up your heart and make you very edgy. Alcohol is a depressant and slows down your reactions, as well as causing liver and brain damage when taken in large amounts over time. If you are striving for fitness, why bother with either of these two poisons?

6 Avoid processed foods – with their added sugar, salt, additives, preservatives and colouring, who needs them? Avoid potato crisps, salted peanuts, chocolate, sweets, processed meats and cheeses, and all packaged and canned food.

7 No sweet puddings – concentrate on fresh fruit and natural yoghurt, which are healthier and lower in calories. It is believed that yoghurt aids digestion and increases resistance to infection.

8 Use a non-stick pan – this will enable you to use less fat (of the polyunsaturated variety, of course) when you *do* fry. Remember to trim off all visible fat when cooking. And here is a tip for pastry-making: use one part fat to three parts flour rather than two parts to one, and your recipes will not suffer.

9 Eat more raw foods – try to eat a salad or some raw vegetables and fresh fruit every day. Scientists have discovered that raw foods play a part in fighting cancer, ulcers, high blood pressure and other modern diseases: they also help ward off diseases and slow down the ageing process.

No.	Food	Inedible waste %	Energy kcal	kJ	Protein g	Fat g	Carbo-hydrate (as mono-saccharide) g
	Milk						
1	Cream – double	0	447	1,841	1.5	48.2	2.0
2	Cream – single	0	195	806	2.4	19.3	3.2
3	Milk, liquid, whole	0	65	272	3.2	3.9	4.6
4	Milk, liquid, skimmed	0	32	137	3.4	0.1	4.7
5	Milk, condensed whole, sweetened	0	170	709	8.5	10.2	11.7
6	Milk, whole, evaporated	0	149	620	8.4	9.4	8.1
7	Milk, dried, skimmed	0	339	1,442	36.1	0.6	50.4
8	Yogurt, low fat, natural	0	65	276	5.1	0.8	10.0
9	Yogurt, low fat, fruit	0	89	382	4.1	0.7	17.9
	Cheese						
10	Cheddar	0	406	1,682	26.0	33.5	0
11	Cottage	0	96	402	13.6	4.0	1.4
12	Cheese spread	0	283	1,173	18.3	22.9	0.9
13	Feta	0	245	1,017	16.5	19.9	0
14	Brie	0	300	1,246	22.8	23.2	0
	Meat						
15	Bacon, rashers, raw	11	339	1,402	13.9	31.5	0
16	Bacon, rashers, grilled	0	393	1,632	28.1	31.2	0
17	Beef, average, raw	17	313	1,296	16.6	27.4	0
18	Beef, mince, stewed	0	229	955	23.1	15.2	0
19	Beef, stewing steak, raw	4	176	736	20.2	10.6	0
20	Beef, stewing steak, cooked	0	223	932	30.9	11.0	0
21	Black pudding, fried	0	305	1,270	12.9	21.9	15.0
22	Chicken, raw	41	194	809	19.7	12.8	0
23	Chicken, roast, meat and skin	0	213	888	24.4	12.8	0
24	Chicken, roast, meat only	0	148	621	24.8	5.4	0
25	Corned beef	0	202	844	25.9	10.9	0
26	Ham	0	166	690	16.4	11.1	0
27	Kidney, pigs, raw	6	86	363	15.5	2.7	0
28	Kidney, pigs, fried	0	202	848	29.2	9.5	0
29	Lamb, average, raw	23	295	1,223	16.2	25.6	0
30	Lamb, roast	0	266	1,106	26.1	17.9	0
31	Liver, lambs, raw	0	140	587	20.3	6.2	0.8
32	Liver, lambs, fried	0	237	989	30.1	12.9	0
33	Luncheon meat	0	266	1,153	12.9	23.8	3.3
34	Paté, average	0	347	1,436	13.7	31.9	1.4
35	Pork, average, raw	26	297	1,231	16.9	25.5	0
36	Pork chop, cooked	26	332	1,380	28.5	24.2	0
37	Sausage, beef, cooked	0	267	1,114	12.9	17.7	15.0
38	Sausage, pork, cooked	0	317	1,318	13.6	24.5	11.2
39	Steak & kidney pie	0	274	1,146	9.3	17.1	22.2
40	Turkey, roast, meat & skin	0	189	793	26.2	9.4	0

Composition per 100g (raw edible weight except where stated)

Water	Calcium mg	Iron mg	Sodium mg	Vitamin A (retinol equivalent) μg	Thia-min mg	Ribo-flavin mg	Niacin equivalent mg	Vitamin C mg	No.
49	50	0.2	30	500	0.02	0.08	0.4	1	1
72	79	0.3	40	155	0.03	0.12	0.8	1	2
88	103	0.1	50	56	0.05	0.17	0.9	1.5	3
91	108	0.1	50	1	0.05	0.18	0.9	1.5	4
30	270	0.2	140	123	0.09	0.46	2.3	4.1	5
69	260	0.3	170	125	0.07	0.42	2.1	1.5	6
3	1,230	0.3	510	550	0.38	0.16	9.5	13.2	7
86	200	0.1	80	12	0.06	0.25	1.2	0.8	8
77	150	0.1	70	12	0.05	0.21	1.2	0.7	9
37	800	0.4	610	363	0.04	0.50	6.2	0	10
79	60	0.1	450	41	0.02	0.19	3.3	0	11
51	510	0.7	1,170	198	0.02	0.24	0.1	0	12
56	384	0.2	1,260	270	0.03	0.11	4.2	0	13
48	380	0.8	1,410	238	0.09	0.60	6.2	0	14
51	7	0.6	1,340	0	0.45	0.14	6.5	0	15
34	14	1.3	2,404	0	0.57	0.27	12.5	0	16
55	7	1.9	70	10	0.05	0.23	6.9	0	17
59	18	3.1	320	0	0.05	0.33	9.3	0	18
69	8	2.1	72	0	0.06	0.23	8.5	0	19
57	15	3.0	360	0	0.03	0.33	10.2	0	20
44	35	20.0	1,210	0	0.09	0.07	3.8	0	21
67	9	0.7	75	0	0.11	0.13	9.6	0	22
62	13	0.5	90	0	0.05	0.19	13.6	0	23
68	9	0.8	81	0	0.08	0.19	12.8	0	24
59	27	2.4	854	0	0	0.20	9.1	0	25
67	4	0.6	1,405	0	0.54	0.20	6.3	0	26
80	10	6.4	200	160	0.56	2.58	11.1	6.5	27
58	12	9.1	220	220	0.41	3.70	20.1	11.9	28
56	7	1.4	71	0	0.09	0.21	7.1	0	29
55	8	2.5	65	0	0.12	0.31	11.0	0	30
70	6	7.5	73	19,900	0.39	4.64	20.7	19.2	31
54	8	10.9	83	30,500	0.38	5.65	24.7	18.6	32
54	39	1.0	913	0	0.06	0.15	3.9	0	33
47	14	8.2	762	8,300	0.14	1.32	4.3	0	34
57	8	0.9	65	0	0.49	0.20	8.9	0	35
46	11	1.2	84	0	0.66	0.20	11.0	0	36
48	68	1.6	1,095	0	0	0.14	9.0	0	37
45	54	1.5	1,075	0	0.01	0.16	7.2	0	38
51	47	1.8	402	0	0.12	0.25	4.9	0	39
63	7	0.9	70	0	0.09	0.16	12.2	0	40

No.	Food	Inedible waste %	Energy kcal	kJ	Protein g	Fat g	Carbo-hydrate (as mono-saccharide) g
	Fish						
41	White fish, filleted	3	77	324	17.1	0.9	0
42	Cod, fried	0	235	982	19.6	14.3	7.5
43	Fish fingers, raw	0	178	749	12.6	7.5	16.1
44	Herrings, whole	46	251	1,040	16.8	20.4	0
45	Mackerel	40	282	1,170	19.0	22.9	0
46	Pilchards, canned in tomato sauce	0	126	531	18.8	5.4	0.7
47	Sardines, canned in oil, fish only	0	217	906	23.7	18.6	0
48	Tuna in oil	0	289	1,202	22.8	22.0	0
49	Prawns, boiled	0	107	451	22.6	1.8	0
	Eggs						
50	Eggs, boiled	12	147	612	12.3	10.9	0
51	Eggs, fried	0	232	961	14.1	19.5	0
	Fats						
52	Butter	0	740	3,041	0.4	82.0	0
53	Lard, cooking fat, dripping	0	892	3,667	0	99.1	0
54	Low fat spread	0	366	1,506	0	40.7	0
55	Margarine, average	0	730	3,000	0.1	81.0	0
56	Cooking and salad oil	0	899	3,696	0	99.9	0
	Preserves, etc.						
57	Chocolate, milk	0	529	2,214	8.4	30.3	59.4
58	Honey	0	288	1,229	0.4	0	76.4
59	Jam	0	262	1,116	0.5	0	69.2
60	Marmalade	0	261	1,114	0.1	0	69.5
61	Sugar, white	0	394	1,680	0	0	105.3
62	Syrup	0	298	1,269	0.3	0	79.0
63	Peppermints	0	392	1,670	0.5	0.7	102.2
	Vegetables						
64	Aubergines	23	14	62	0.7	0	3.1
65	Baked beans	0	81	345	4.8	0.6	15.1
66	Beans, runner, boiled	1	19	83	1.9	0.2	2.7
67	Beans, red kidney, raw	0	272	1,159	22.1	1.7	45.0
68	Beans, soya, boiled	0	141	592	12.4	6.4	9.0
69	Beetroot, boiled	0	44	189	1.8	0	9.9
70	Brussels sprouts, boiled	0	18	75	2.8	0	1.7
71	Cabbage, raw	43	22	92	2.8	0	2.8
72	Cabbage, boiled	0	15	66	1.7	0	2.3
73	Carrots, old	4	23	98	0.7	0	5.4
74	Cauliflower, cooked	0	9	40	1.6	0	0.8
75	Celery	27	8	36	0.9	0	1.3
76	Courgettes, raw	13	29	122	1.6	0.4	5.0

Composition per 100g

Water g	Calcium mg	Iron mg	Sodium mg	Vitamin A (retinol equivalent) μg	Thia-min mg	Ribo-flavin mg	Niacin equivalent mg	Vitamin C mg	No.
82	22	0.5	99	1	0.07	0.09	6.0	0	41
57	80	0.5	100	0	0.06	0.07	4.9	0	42
64	43	0.7	320	0.2	0.09	0.06	3.5	0	43
64	33	0.8	67	46	0	0.18	7.2	0	44
57	24	1.0	130	45	0.09	0.35	11.6	0	45
74	300	2.7	370	8	0.02	0.29	11.1	0	46
58	550	2.9	650	7	0.04	0.36	12.6	0	47
55	7	1.1	420	0	0.04	0.11	17.2	0	48
70	150	1.1	1,590	0	0.03	0.03	7.4	0	49
75	52	2.0	140	190	0.09	0.47	3.7	0	50
63	64	2.5	220	140	0.07	0.42	4.2	0	51
15	15	0.2	870	985	0	0	0.1	0	52
1	1	0.1	2	0	0	0	0	0	53
51	0	0	690	900	0	0	0	0	54
16	4	0.3	800	860	0	0	0.1	0	55
0	0	0	0	0	0	0	0	0	56
2	220	1.6	120	6.6	0.10	0.23	1.6	0	57
23	5	0.4	11	0	0	0.05	0.2	0	58
30	18	1.2	14	2	0	0	0	10	59
28	35	0.6	18	8	0	0	0	10	60
0	2	0	0	0	0	0	0	0	61
28	26	1.5	270	0	0	0	0	0	62
0	7	0.2	9	0	0	0	0	0	63
93	10	0.4	3	0	0.05	0.03	1.0	5	64
74	48	1.4	550	12	0.08	0.06	1.3	0	65
91	22	0.7	1	67	0.03	0.07	0.8	5	66
11	140	6.7	40	0	0.54	0.18	5.5	0	67
67	145	2.5	15	0	0.26	0.16	3.4	0	68
83	30	0.4	64	0	0.02	0.04	0.4	5	69
92	25	0.5	2	67	0.06	0.10	0.9	40	70
88	57	0.6	7	50	0.06	0.05	0.8	55	71
93	38	0.4	4	50	0.03	0.03	0.5	20	72
90	48	0.6	95	2,000	0.06	0.05	0.7	6	73
95	18	0.4	4	5	0.06	0.06	0.8	20	74
94	52	0.6	140	0	0.03	0.03	0.5	7	75
92	30	1.5	1	58	0.05	0.09	0.6	16	76

No.	Food	Inedible waste %	Energy kcal	kJ	Protein g	Fat g	Carbo-hydrate (as mono-saccharide) g
77	Cucumber	23	10	43	0.6	0.1	1.8
78	Lentils, cooked	0	99	420	7.6	0.5	17.0
79	Lettuce	30	12	51	1.0	0.4	1.2
80	Mushrooms	25	13	53	1.8	0.6	0
81	Onion	3	23	99	0.9	0	5.2
82	Parsnips, cooked	0	56	238	1.3	0	13.5
83	Peas, frozen, boiled	0	72	307	6.0	0.9	10.7
84	Peas, canned processed	0	86	366	6.9	0.7	18.9
85	Peppers, green	14	12	51	0.9	0	2.2
86	Potatoes	10[1] 20[2]	74	315	2.0	0.2	17.1
87	Potatoes, boiled	0	76	322	1.8	0.1	18.0
88	Potato crisps	0	533	2,224	6.3	35.9	49.3
89	Potatoes, fried (chips)	0	234	983	3.6	10.2	34.0
90	Potatoes, oven chips	0	162	687	3.2	4.2	29.8
91	Potatoes, roast	0	150	632	3.0	4.5	25.9
92	Spinach, boiled	0	30	128	5.1	0.5	1.4
93	Sweetcorn, canned	0	85	379	2.9	1.2	16.8
94	Sweet potato	14	91	387	1.2	0.6	21.5
95	Tomatoes, fresh	0	14	60	0.9	0	2.8
96	Turnips, cooked	0	14	60	0.7	0.3	2.3
97	Watercress	23	14	61	2.9	0	0.7
98	Yam, boiled	0	119	508	1.6	0.1	29.8
	Fruit						
99	Apples	20	46	196	0.3	0	11.9
100	Apricots, canned in syrup	0	106	452	0.5	0	27.7
101	Apricots, dried	0	182	772	4.8	0	43.4
102	Avocado pear	29	223	922	4.2	22.2	1.8
103	Bananas	40	76	326	1.1	0	19.2
104	Blackcurrants	2	28	121	0.9	0	6.6
105	Cherries	13	47	201	0.6	0	11.9
106	Dates, dried	14	248	1,056	2.0	0	63.9
107	Figs, dried	0	213	908	3.6	0	52.9
108	Gooseberries, cooked, unsweetened	0	14	62	0.9	0	2.9
109	Grapes	5	63	268	0.6	0	16.1
110	Grapefruit	50	22	95	0.6	0	5.3
111	Lemon juice	64	7	31	0.3	0	1.6
112	Mango	34	59	253	0.5	0	15.3
113	Melon	40	23	97	0.8	0	5.2
114	Oranges	25	35	150	0.8	0	8.5
115	Orange juice	0	38	161	0.6	0	9.4
116	Peaches	13	37	156	0.6	0	9.1
117	Peaches, canned in syrup	0	87	373	0.4	0	22.9
118	Pears	28	41	175	0.3	0	10.6

[1] Old potatoes   [2] New potatoes

Composition per 100g

Water g	Calcium mg	Iron mg	Sodium mg	Vitamin A (retinol equivalent) μg	Thia-min mg	Ribo-flavin mg	Niacin equivalent mg	Vitamin C mg	No.
96	23	0.3	13	0	0.04	0.04	0.3	8	77
72	13	2.4	12	3	0.11	0.04	1.6	0	78
96	23	0.9	9	167	0.07	0.08	0.4	15	79
92	3	1.0	9	0	0.10	0.40	4.6	3	80
93	31	0.3	10	0	0.03	0.05	0.4	10	81
83	36	0.5	4	0	0.07	0.06	0.9	10	82
78	35	1.6	2	50	0.30	0.09	1.6	12	83
70	33	1.8	380	10	0.10	0.04	1.4	0	84
94	9	0.4	2	33	0.08	0.03	0.9	100	85
79	8	0.4	8	0	0.20	0.02	1.5	8-19	86
80	4	0.4	7	0	0.20	0.02	1.2	5-9	87
3	37	2.1	550	0	0.19	0.07	6.1	17	88
44	14	0.84	41	0	0.2	0.02	1.5	6-14	89
59	1	0.8	53	0	0.1	0.04	3.1	12	90
65	10	0.62	9	0	0.2	0.02	1.3	5-12	91
85	136	4.0	120	1,000	0.07	0.15	1.8	25	92
72	4	0.5	270	4	0.04	0.06	1.8	0	93
70	22	0.7	19	4,000[3]	0.10	0.06	1.2	25	94
93	13	0.4	3	100	0.06	0.04	0.8	20	95
95	55	0.4	28	0	0.03	0.04	0.6	17	96
91	220	1.6	60	500	0.10	0.10	1.1	60	97
66	9	0.3	17	2	0.05	0.01	0.8	2	98
84	4	0.3	2	5	0.04	0.02	0.1	5	99
68	12	0.7	1	166	0.02	0.01	0.4	2	100
15	92	4.1	56	600	0	0.2	3.8	0	101
69	15	1.5	2	17	0.10	0.10	1.8	15	102
71	7	0.4	1	33	0.04	0.07	0.8	10	103
77	60	1.3	3	33	0.03	0.06	0.4	200	104
82	16	0.4	3	20	0.05	0.07	0.4	5	105
15	68	1.6	5	10	0.07	0.04	2.9	0	106
17	280	4.2	87	8	0.10	0.08	2.2	0	107
90	24	0.3	2	25	0.03	0.03	0.5	31	108
79	19	0.3	2	0	0.04	0.02	0.3	4	109
91	17	0.3	1	0	0.05	0.02	0.3	40	110
91	8	0.1	2	0	0.02	0.01	0.1	50	111
83	10	0.5	7	200	0.03	0.04	0.4	30	112
94	16	0.4	17	175	0.05	0.03	0.3	50	113
86	41	0.3	3	8	0.10	0.03	0.3	50	114
88	12	0.3	2	8	0.08	0.02	0.3	25-45	115
86	5	0.4	3	83	0.02	0.05	1.1	8	116
74	4	0.4	1	41	0.01	0.02	0.6	4	117
83	8	0.2	2	2	0.03	0.03	0.3	3	118

[3] The vitamin A content of white and yellow varieties may vary between 0 and 12,000 μg

NUTRITION FOR WEIGHT-TRAINING

No.	Food	Inedible waste %	Energy kcal	kJ	Protein g	Fat g	Carbo-hydrate (as mono-saccharide) g
119	Pineapple, canned in juice	0	46	194	0.5	0	11.6
120	Plums	8	32	137	0.6	0	7.9
121	Prunes, dried	17	161	686	2.4	0	40.3
122	Raspberries	0	25	105	0.9	0	5.6
123	Rhubarb, cooked with sugar	0	45	191	0.5	0	11.4
124	Strawberries	3	26	109	0.6	0	6.2
125	Sultanas	0	250	1,066	1.8	0	64.7
	Nuts						
126	Almonds	63	565	2,336	16.9	53.5	4.3
127	Coconut, desiccated	0	604	2,492	5.6	62.0	6.4
128	Peanuts, roasted & salted	0	570	2,364	24.3	49.0	8.6
	Cereals						
129	Biscuits, chocolate	0	524	2,197	5.7	27.6	67.4
130	Biscuits, plain, digestive	0	471	1,978	6.3	20.9	68.6
131	Biscuits, semi-sweet	0	457	1,925	6.7	16.6	74.8
132	Bread, brown	0	217	924	8.4	2.0	44.2
133	Bread, white	0	230	980	8.2	1.7	48.6
134	Bread, wholemeal	0	215	911	9.0	2.5	41.6
	Breakfast cereals						
135	Cornflakes	0	368	1,567	8.6	1.6	85.1
136	Weetabix	0	340	1,444	11.4	3.4	70.3
137	Muesli	0	368	1,556	12.9	7.5	66.2
138	Cream crackers	0	440	1,857	9.5	16.3	68.3
139	Crispbread, rye	0	321	1,367	9.4	2.1	70.6
140	Flour, white	0	337	1,435	9.4	1.3	76.7
141	Flour, wholemeal	0	306	1,302	12.7	2.2	62.8
142	Oats, porridge	0	374	1,582	10.9	9.2	66.0
143	Rice, raw	0	359	1,529	7.0	1.0	85.8
144	Spaghetti, raw	0	342	1,456	12.0	1.8	74.1
	Cakes, etc						
145	Chocolate cake with butter icing	0	500	2,092	5.8	30.9	53.1
146	Currant buns	0	296	1,250	7.6	7.5	52.7
147	Fruit cake, rich	0	322	1,357	4.9	12.5	50.7
148	Jam tarts	0	368	1,552	3.3	13.0	63.4
149	Plain cake, Madeira	0	393	1,652	5.4	16.9	58.4

Composition per 100g

Water g	Calcium mg	Iron mg	Sodium mg	Vitamin A (retinol equivalent) μg	Thia-min mg	Ribo-flavin mg	Niacin equivalent mg	Vitamin C mg	No.
77	12	0.4	1	7	0.08	0.02	0.3	20-40	119
85	12	0.3	2	37	0.05	0.03	0.6	3	120
23	38	2.9	12	160	0.10	0.20	1.9	0	121
83	41	1.2	3	13	0.02	0.03	0.5	25	122
85	84	0.3	2	8	0	0.03	0.4	7	123
89	22	0.7	2	5	0.02	0.03	0.5	60	124
18	52	1.8	53	5	0.10	0.08	0.6	0	125
5	250	4.2	6	0	0.24	0.92	4.7	0	126
2	22	3.6	28	0	0.06	0.04	1.8	0	127
5	61	2.0	440	0	0.23	0.10	21.3	0	128
2.2	110	1.7	160	0	0.03	0.13	2.7	0	129
2.5	92	3.2	600	0	0.14	0.11	2.4	0	130
2.5	120	2.1	410	0	0.13	0.08	2.9	0	131
40	99	2.2	540	0	0.27	0.10	2.3	0	132
38	105	1.6	525	0	0.21	0.06	2.3	0	133
38	54	2.7	560	0	0.34	0.09	1.8	0	134
3.0	3	6.7	1,160	0	1.8	1.6	21.9	0	135
1.8	33	7.6	360	0	1.0	1.5	14.3	0	136
5.8	200	4.6	180	0	0.33	0.27	5.7	0	137
4.3	110	1.7	610	0	0.13	0.08	3.4	0	138
6.4	50	3.7	220	0	0.28	0.14	2.9	0	139
14.0	140	2.0	2	0	0.31	0.04	3.5	0	140
14.0	38	3.9	2	0	0.47	0.09	8.3	0	141
8.2	52	3.8	9	0	0.90	0.09	3.3	0	142
11.4	4	0.5	4	0	0.41	0.02	5.8	0	143
9.8	25	2.1	3	0	0.22	0.03	3.1	0	144
8.4	130	1.6	440	298	0.07	0.09	2.0	0	145
27.7	110	1.9	230	0	0.37	0.16	3.1	0	146
20.6	84	3.2	220	0	0.07	0.09	1.3	0	147
14.4	72	1.7	130	0	0.06	0.02	1.2	0	148
20.2	42	1.1	380	0	0.06	0.11	1.6	0	149

Unfortunately, we can only supply details for Great Britain. Readers in other countries will have to contact their national sports bodies for information.

British Amateur Weight-Lifters' Association (BAWLA)

Contact: Mr W. Holland, General Secretary, 3 Iffley Turn, Oxford OX4 4DU. Tel: 0865 778319

This organization can provide details of weight-training courses in all the BAWLA-registered clubs, and offers weight-training proficiency awards for men and women. It is the only official body for instructors and coaches, on an amateur, professional and schools level, offering a 'Leader's award' for instructors teaching weight-training in gyms and clubs, and a 'Teacher's award' for the proper instruction of weight-training in schools. BAWLA specialize in power-lifting and the Olympic lifts, but they also cover the broader field of weight-training. Their magazine is called *The Strength Athlete*. There is a membership and club fee, which varies from region to region.

National Amateur Bodybuilders' Association (NABBA)

Contact: Oscar Heidenstam, 30 Craven Street, The Strand, London WC2N 5NT. Tel: 01 839 3554, but best to send SAE for any information required.

This long-established group have been around since 1905, after the demise of the 'Health and Strength League'. They are limited to the British Isles, but since 1982, they have been affiliated with NABBA International. They are interested solely in bodybuilding, and can put their members in touch with 425 clubs on their register, as well as offer advice to those members who train at home. They also provide dates and addresses of contests and shows. In September they hold both the amateur and professional 'Mr

Universe' contests and in May of every year the Mr and Miss NABBA Britain contests. Their magazine is called *Sport and Fitness* (published by Edward Hankey); it is available in newsagents or by annual subscription. Life membership is available.

English Federation of Bodybuilders (EFBB)

Contact: Marilyn Davis, Secretary, The Exchange, Bamtry Road, Wickersley, Rotherham, South Yorkshire. Tel: 0924 376906

This is another bodybuilding organization, founded in 1980, which is affiliated with the International Federation of Bodybuilders (IFBB). There are 127 countries involved. They can direct members towards good training gyms and well-qualified instructors as well as inform them about shows. The European Championships (Mr and Miss Olympia) are held in November. The EFBB is primarily concerned with diet as related to competition, but they also cover every kind of exercise related to bodybuilding. Their magazine, *Muscle & Co.* (by Muscle & Co. publications) is published monthly, and has a section for women. Annual or life membership is available. Fees also entitle members to enter all competitions free.

Association for Health & Exercise Teachers (ASSET)

Contact: Tricia Ligget, East Cottage Studio, Ashendene, Bayford, Herts SG13 8PZ. Tel: 099 286 224

ASSET is the amalgamation of two former groups (CAPET and IDEAS) that work with national bodies concerned with exercise and health. Their aim is to establish acceptable levels of training for instructors, and to encourage an exchange of information among teachers and members of the general public. They are also working on some form of accreditation for instructors. An annual membership fee brings you

their quarterly magazine and information on seminars and workshops. One such workshop is 'An Introduction to Weight-training', and demonstrates the right way to use weight-training equipment as well as showing how to put a programme of exercise together.

Sports Council

Contact: Chris Middleton, 16 Upper Woburn Place, London WC1H 0QP. Tel: 01 388 1277

The Sports Council is a good source of general information, and would refer a potential weight-trainer to the appropriate gym or training club in his/her area.

Physical Education Association of Great Britain and Northern Ireland

Contact: Mr Petheric, 162 Kings Cross Road, London WC1 9DH. Tel: 01 278 9311

This group sets up projects for increasing education in schools on fitness awareness, and devises exercise courses (practical and theoretical) for instructors at various regional centres. They can also provide weight-trainers with information on where to train.

YMCA

Contact: Hugh Owen or Barry Cronin, London Central, 112 Great Russell Street, London WC1B 3NQ. Tel: 01 637 8131

The YMCA offers both beginner's and intermediate weight-training courses to its members. Each course is usually taught over six weeks (lunch-times and evenings), for one hour a week, and covers machines as well as free weights. During the rest of the week, you are asked to consolidate what you have learned by attending two practice sessions. All the instructors are highly qualified, and programmes are worked out on an individual basis. When you reach an advanced level, extra tuition is free.

BIBLIOGRAPHY

Books

Bartlett, E.G., *Weight-Training*, David and Charles, 1984.

Bassey, E.J., and Fentem, P.H., *Exercise: The Facts*, Oxford University Press, 1981.

Berger, Richard A., *Introduction to Weight-Training*, Prentice-Hall, Inc., 1984.

Cheshire, Carolyn, *Body Chic*, Pelham Books Ltd., 1985.

Day, Joanne, *Weider Weight-Training for Women – Better Body Better Shape*, Hamlyn Publishing, 1985.

Fitness Advisory Bureau, *KTG Keeping Fit – for all Ages*, A & C Black Publishers Ltd., 1984.

Fodor, R.V., *Winning Weightlifting*, Sterling Publishing Co. Inc., 1983.

Hazeldine, Rex, *Fitness for Sport*, The Crowood Press, 1985.

Heidenstam, Oscar (of *Health and Strength* magazine), *Muscle Building for Beginners*, W. Foulsham & Co. Ltd., 1981.

Heidenstam, Oscar, *Body Beautiful*, W. Foulsham & Co. Ltd., 1984.

Kennedy, Robert, *Start Bodybuilding – The Complete Natural Program*, Sterling Publishing Co. Inc., 1980.

Kirkley, George, *Success in Weight-Training*, John Murray, 1980.

Kirkley, George and Goodbody, John, *The Manual of Weight-Training*, Stanley Paul & Co. Ltd., 1967.

Lear, J., *Weightlifting*, A & C Black Publishers Ltd., 1980.

Lear, J., *Powerlifters' Manual*, A & C Black Publishers Ltd., 1982.

Lear, J., *KTG Weight-Training*, A & C Black Publishers Ltd., 1984 (produced in collaboration with BAWLA).

Lear, J. and Murray, A., *Power Training for Sport*, B.T. Batsford Ltd.; (1981 hardback; 1983 paperback).

Leen, Edie, *Strength Training for Beauty*, Anderson World Books, Inc., 1983.

Luscombe, Marilyn, *Designer Body – The Bodybuilding Handbook for Women*, Panther Books, 1985.

Lycholat, Tony, *Weight-Training for Women*, Thorsons Publishers Ltd.

Lycholat, Tony, *Weight-Training for Men*, Thorsons Publishers Ltd.

Mazzurco, Philip, *Exerstyle – The Ultimate Guide to Personal Gym Equipment*, Windward, 1985.

Murray, A. and Lear, J., *BAWLA Handbook for Instructors*, BAWLA publication.

O'Sullivan, Susanne, *Fully Fit in 60 Minutes a Week – The Complete Shape-Up Programme for Women*, Thorsons Publishers Ltd., 1983.

Payne, Howard, *Weight-Training for All Sports*, Pelham Books, 1979.

Popplewell, G., *Modern Weightlifting and Powerlifting*, Faber.

Reynolds, Bill, *Complete Weight-Training Book*, Anderson World Books, Inc., 1976.

Schwartz, L., *Heavyhands. The Ultimate Exercise*, Pelham Books, 1983.

Sobey, Edwin and Burns, Gary, *Runner's World: Aerobic Weight-Training Book*, Runner's World Books, 1982.

Sobey, Edwin, *Runner's World: Strength Training Book*, Runner's World Books, 1981.

Syer, John, and Connally, Christopher, *Sporting Body, Sporting Mind*, Cambridge University Press, 1984.

Tancred, Bill, and Tancred, Geoff, *Weight-Training for Sport*, Hodder and Stoughton, 1984.

Whitehead, Dr N.J., *EP Sport – Conditioning for Sport*, A & C Black Publishers Ltd., 1975.

Magazines

Most of the magazines mentioned below are available from general or specialist newsagents. However, some may have to be ordered by subscription from the publisher.

Bodybuilding Monthly, published monthly by Demland Graphics Ltd., West Yorkshire.

Bodypower, published monthly by Multi Language Publications Ltd., London.

Feeling Great, published monthly by the Haymarket Group Ltd., New York.

Fitness, published monthly by Cover Publications Ltd., London.

Flex, published monthly by Joe Weider, California.

Healthy Life News, published by The Marketing Factory, New South Wales.

Healthy Living, published monthly by Askin Publications Ltd., London.

Muscle & Co. (the official journal of the EFBB), published monthly by Muscle & Co. Publications, London.

Muscle and Fitness, (Joe Weider's), published by I Brute Enterprises, California.

Musclemag, (Bob Kennedy's), published monthly by Body Sculpture Barbell Co. Ltd., Ontario.

New Health, published monthly by Haymarket Publishing Ltd., Middlesex.

New Zealand Athlete, published monthly, available from PO Box 56226, Dominion Road, Auckland.

New Zealand Sports and Leisure, published monthly, available from PO Box 109, Otaki.

Prevention, published monthly by Federal Publishing Co. PTY Ltd., New South Wales.

Shape, published monthly by Shape Magazine Inc., California.

Sport and Fitness (NABBA's official publication incorporating *Health and Strength*), published by Edward Hankey, English language edition; parent company, Sport and Fitness-Verlag West Germany.

Sports Fitness, (Joe Weider's), published monthly by Sports Fitness Inc., California.

The Strength Athlete, (BAWLA's publication), published monthly by Pullum, 22 Dunsley Road, Luton, Beds.

Workout, published monthly by VVV Publications Ltd., London.

GLOSSARY

Abduction – The pulling away of certain muscles from the median axis of the body (such as an arm or a leg).

Active exercise – Exercising by the patient himself without any assistance by another person.

Additives – Any of a group of substances (preservatives, emulsifiers, flavourings, colourings, stabilisers and sweeteners) added to food to supposedly improve its flavour and appearance and extend its shelf life.

Adduction – To draw or pull a muscle towards the median axis of the body (such as an arm or a leg).

Adrenalin – A hormone secreted by the adrenal medulla in response to stress that increases heart and pulse rate and blood pressure, and raises the blood levels of glucose and lipids.

Aerobics – Exercise concerned with cardiovascular strength involving intake of oxygen.

All-body approach – Using all the body's main muscle groups.

Anaerobics – Exercise concerned mainly with the development of muscle and explosive power. Extra intake of oxygen not a characteristic.

Anorexia nervosa – A psychological disorder characterized by fear of becoming fat and refusal of food, which can lead to debility and death.

Antagonists (muscles) – Opposing muscle groups.

Antenatal – Occurring or present before birth.

Assisted exercise – Active movement of a limb with assistance by the other limb (auto-assistance), or with the assistance of another person.

Atrophy – A wasting away of an organ or muscle through disease, faulty nutrition or lack of use.

Barbell – A length of tempered steel – 1.37m/4ft 6in in length usually – to which collars and poundage are added.

Biceps – The muscle that flexes the forearm, more commonly known as the upper arm muscle.

Bodybuilding – A sport that strives to improve the aesthetic appearance of the body in terms of muscle mass and symmetry.

Body Ess – A hydraulic type of weight-training equipment, light to moderate weights, for home use.

Calisthenics – Light exercises designed to promote general fitness and develop muscle tone.

Calorie – A unit of heat, equal to 4,1868 joules; it is the quantity of heat required to raise the temperature of 1 gram of water by 1°c.

Cam-type machine – A cam is a rotating cylinder with an irregular profile, attached to a revolving shaft to give a reciprocating motion to a part in contact with it.

Carbohydrate – Any of a large group of organic compounds (including sugars, cellulose, glycogen and starch) that are an important source of food and energy for animals.

Cheat style – Loosely applied style.

Cholesterol – A waxy, insoluble, pale yellow substance found in all animal tissues (some manufactured by the liver, some obtained from food) that is a forerunner of other body steroids. Evidence links high levels of cholesterol to heart disease.

Collar – Metal locking device.

Cross education (or bilateral transfer) – This refers to the ability of the nervous system to transfer some of the effects achieved by one part of the body to the bilaterally opposite part.

Cuts – A slang term for muscle definition, especially used in bodybuilding.

Dumb-bell – This is a 38-45cm/15-18in rod of steel, to which collars and poundage are added. It enables single-arm movements.

Enzyme – A group of complex proteins produced by living cells that act as catalysts in specific biochemical reactions.

Fats – A group of naturally occurring soft, greasy solids, present in some plants and in the tissues of animals, that form a reserve energy source.

Fibre (or roughage) – The coarse indigestible parts of food that provide bulk to the diet and aid digestion.

Free weights – Cast iron discs with central 1in hole, ranging from 1¼kg to 25kg.

Gastrochnemius – Latin for upper calf muscle.

Glucose – Known as 'blood sugar', because it is (stored as either glycogen or fat) a form of sugar found in abundance in the bloodstream, a major energy source in metabolism.

Haemoglobin – A protein that gives red blood cells their colour; it combines with oxygen to carry it to the tissues.

Hydraulics – Resistance needs to be pushed back to starting point.

Hormones – The body's chemical messengers, controlled by the brain.

Insulin – A protein hormone, secreted by the pancreas, that controls glucose levels in the blood.

Isokinetic exercise – This is an accommodating variable resistance in which the speed of motion is set and the resistance accommodates to match the force applied.

Isometric – Muscles contracted without any movements of the parts of the body carrying out the contractions.

Isotonic – Produces joint movement; the contracting muscle shortens and this produces the movement.

Lats – Short for 'Latissimus dorsi', which are the muscles of the back, below the shoulder.

Load curve – Graph of muscle's strength through movement; hard at first, easier later.

Manual resistance – The first stage of resistance exercises, wherein a therapist provides his/her own hand against which a patient pushes his/her weakened muscle.

Manual resistive exercise – Therapist adjusts the speed of movement and resistance to suit the patient's needs at a particular stage of rehabilitation.

Masolet Sequence Training – Weight-training on five pieces of apparatus on a circuit; devised by two Norwegian physiotherapists.

Metabolism – Process by which digested nutrients are turned into building blocks and energy for the body.

Mineral – A group of naturally occurring solids, inorganic substances with a characteristic crystalline form.

Muscle-bound – Having overdeveloped, inelastic muscle lacking in flexibility.

Mutagent – Any substance that can cause a change or mutation in a cell.

Passive exercise – The movement of a part of the body by another person without any effort by the injured person.

Physiology – That branch of science concerned with the functioning of organisms.

Physiotherapy – The therapeutic use of certain physical agents such as massage, exercise, etc.

Plasma – The clear yellowish fluid portion of the blood or lymph in which the corpuscles and cells are suspended.

Postnatal – Occurring after birth.

Proprioception – The feeling of 'balance' experienced by the receptors within the joints.

Protein – A chain of amino acids, twenty three in all, which are essential in the make-up of living organisms and essential for growth and cellular repair. Nine are obtained from food; the other fourteen are made in the body.

Preacher curl bench – A special bench with the upper half permanently raised to allow a biceps exercise with dumb-bell to take place.

Quadriceps – Major thigh muscle.

RDA (Recommended Daily Amount) – A standard established by a country's governing health body to establish minimum levels of intake of substances such as vitamins and minerals.

Reps (Repetitions) – The number of times a movement is performed.

Resistance – Any force that impedes motion; used in physiotherapy to cause a muscle to exercise either against itself or against an object or piece of equipment.

Resisted exercises – Exercises performed against a resistive force; can be isometric or isotonic in nature.

Roman chair – A special piece of machinery used for an advanced abdominal exercise.

Set – A unit containing a fixed number of repetitions.

Strength curve – When a resistance or weight is moved through the whole range of a muscle's movement, and the effort or strength is not even or consistent throughout.

Strict style – Performing by the book.

Support pin – The small metal bar that slots into the weight-stack of an exercise machine, allowing you to lift only the weight you require.

Swingbell – A 38cm/15in rod of steel with discs centrally positioned to enable grips at both ends for certain overhead or swinging movements.

Testosterone – Male hormones responsible for growth, and building and strengthening of muscle. Low concentration in women.

Tibialis anterior – The muscle at the front of the leg.

Triceps – The muscle at the back of the upper arm.

Ultrasound – Ultrasonic waves of the same nature as sound used in medical diagnosis and therapy.

Valsalva manoeuvre – Holding your breath during exercise causing increased pressure within chest cavity. This causes a rapid rise in blood pressure, which, in turn, diminishes the cardiac output and slows the venous return. A rapid decrease in blood pressure results, possibly causing dizziness, faintness, headache and even blackout.

Variable resistance – Resistance adjusts to differences in muscle strength occurring at various points in a movement.

Vastus medials – The muscle that locks the knee into full extension.

Vena cava – The main vein returning blood to the heart.

Vitamin – A group of substances essential in small quantities for body metabolism. They occur naturally in certain foods; insufficient supply of any leads to deficiency diseases.

Weight-lifting – Use of weights for the development of muscle mass.

Weight-stack – The weight lifted by a weight-training machine, usually stacked in bars of kilo weight.

Weight-training – Use of weights for toning muscle.

INDEX

Acknowledgements

We would like to thank Denise Lewis at the Big Apple Health Studio, London, for all her help in devising Heavyhands (pages 101, 103, 104 and 105) and warm-up exercise sequences (page 13) for the book, and also for allowing us to use the studio and some of the instructors in the photography. Denise's method is recognised by the British Keep-Fit Confederation.

We would also like to thank Rob Walker of Central London Polytechnic, and Burtons Gym, London, for their kind assistance and cooperation (pages 50-64), and our models Janice and Peter Townson who performed the exercises in Chapter 3.

Our thanks also to 'Sports Pages' of New Compton Street, London, for their help in compiling the bibliography.

Nutritional tables

The tables on pages 146-153 are reproduced from the *Manual of Nutrition* by kind permission of the Controller of Her Majesty's Stationery Office.

Illustrations

All the graphic illustrations included in the book are copyright of Bruce Algra and are reproduced by courtesy of International Sport and Leisure Marketing Ltd – pages 16, 17, 22, 23, 27, 30, 31, 32, 33, 34, 35, 36, 37, 38, 39, 40, 41, 42, 43, 45, 107, 109 and 111.

The illustrations and figures on pages 24, 25, 28, 29, 72 and 76 are by Phil Evans.

We would also like to thank Mr Peter Hunt of Masolet (UK) Ltd for the Masolet sequence of diagrams on pages 134 and 135.

Photographs

We would like to thank the following for supplying photographic material for use in the book:
Big Apple Health Studio: pages 104 and 105
Bolton Stirland International Ltd: pages 46, 94 and 96
Shabnam Chaudhri: page 81
Club Mediterranée: page 120
David: page 87
Richard Gardner: pages 70 and 71
Ron Hill Sports: page 116
Tommy Hindley: pages 116 and 118
Hydrafitness: page 88
International Sport and Leisure Marketing Ltd: pages 89, 90, 91, 92 and 111
Kent Photonews: page 67
Rose Macdonald: pages 123, 124, 126, 127, 128 and 133
Multigym: page 47
Olympus Sport: pages 117 and 121
Open Rugby Magazine: page 119
Powersport International Ltd: front cover and pages 11, 49, 83, 84, 85, 86 and 95
Alan Roberts: back cover and pages 13, 21, 69, 101, 103 and 113
Schnell (UK) Ltd: pages 47 and 93
Mark Shearman: pages 99, 114, 115 and 117
Sport Engineering: page 15
Sports Council: pages 8, 9, 74 and 97
Paul Stimpson: page 137
Chris Taylor: front cover and pages 50, 51, 52, 53, 54, 55, 56, 57, 58, 59, 60, 61, 62, 63 and 64
Universal Home Gym: page 97

International Sport and Leisure Marketing Ltd

If you need further information on the equipment and products mentioned throughout the book, please contact:
International Sport and Leisure Marketing Ltd,
Unit 1,
TPN Warehouse,
Quarry Road,
Godstone,
Surrey RH9 9DQ
Telephone: (0833) 844120/844108
Telex: 8952 022 CTYTELG

In the United States, contact:
Fitnus,
3125 19th Street,
Suite 305,
Bakersfield,
California 93301,
USA
Telephone: (805) 832-7317